THE LOST LANDSCAPE

Other Books by Winifred Welles

THE HESITANT HEART

THIS DELICATE LOVE

SKIPPING ALONG ALONE

BLOSSOMING ANTLERS

A SPECTACLE FOR SCHOLARS

THE PARK THAT SPRING FORGOT

THE SHAPE OF MEMORY

THE LOST LANDSCAPE

Some Memories of a Family and a Town in Connecticut
1659-1906

by
WINIFRED WELLES

Illustrated by Phyllis Coté

NEW YORK : HENRY HOLT AND COMPANY

First and second printings before publication

PRINTED IN THE UNITED STATES OF AMERICA

For J. W. S.

FOREWORD

EXCEPT for historical figures, no actual surnames have been used for any of the characters in this book. Many of the incidents have been remembered, either by myself or by others, and also some have been imagined.

For descriptions of events and customs in the past I am most indebted to the following: Histories of Norwich and New London by Miss Frances E. Caulkins, *Old Houses of the Antient Town of Norwich* by Miss Mary E. Perkins, and a pamphlet on Dr. Philip Turner of Norwich by Dr. Charles B. Graves of New London.

W. W.

CONTENTS

PART I

PART II

PART III

PART I

CHAPTER I

A BIRTHDAY

IT ALWAYS seemed to me that I could remember the night when I was born. I refused to believe that because I had heard the story so many times, I had merely learned it by heart. At least nobody could deny that I had been present on that evening. So I became convinced that I had been made aware during the event, by some special arrangement with a good witch or an amiable angel, of each person's part in it, particularly my father's heroic one.

Since it was winter and Connecticut, there must have

been snow on the ground, and steely stars pricking the black sky arched over the house, and the branches of the maple trees standing rigid in the cold. Both upstairs and down lamps would have been lit, so that more windows than usual were ruddy against the dark. To anyone crossing the iron bridge across the river or passing on the road, the house might have appeared twinkling and expectant.

My mother lay upstairs in the front bedroom over the parlor, her face white against the white pillow, her long braid of dark-gold hair trailing over the edge of the bed. Mrs. Robinson, the nurse, a starched, austere woman, moved softly rustling around the room, going down now and then to the kitchen to complete preparations with Hannah. Mrs. Robinson was one of the sybilline priestesses attached to the ritual of birth considered so indispensable by the genteel women of Norwich during the nineties—or for that matter the eighties—since her time of service had been long and honorable.

"I suppose you will have Mrs. Robinson?" would be the confident inquiry of friends months before "the time."

"Oh, indeed yes!" was the inevitable reply. "You know she has had *hundreds* of babies!"

She was so constant a guest in some of the homes—practically a perennial bloom, in fact—that she needed little direction, always remembering the servants' names, the idiosyncrasies of the members of each household, and most valuable of all, "where things were kept."

To have had one of the few available hospital nurses of that time would not have been considered quite respectable. It was thought, in my mother's time, that women who merely received training of some ambiguous institutional variety could not compare favorably with Mrs. Robinson, who had had so much experience in the homes —and always the very nicest homes. Moreover, she was a matron and she had borne children herself—facts that greatly enhanced confidence in her capacity for wisdom as well as in her often-proved powers of patience and skill. No, the ladies of Norwich could not have endured the torture and the humiliation of childbirth in the presence of anyone young and strong, not so long as they could call on Mrs. Robinson, that battle-scarred widow whose face and figure were as familiar as the Soldier's Monument.

Downstairs, early that evening, Fred and Hannah sat in the kitchen finishing their supper. Hannah's plain Yankee face with its gold-rimmed spectacles was soberer than usual, and she stirred her tea slowly and thoughtfully. Fred too had little to say, sitting hunched over in his chair, now and then making little sucking sounds with his tongue in his teeth. Hannah knew that he must stay there with her in the kitchen until it was time to send for the Doctor, but she may have wished that he could have waited elsewhere. Alone, she would have solaced herself and turned her mind from anxiety by reading in an old copy of *The Age of Fable; or Beauties of Mythology* by Thomas Bulfinch. This and the Bible provided her only intellectual excursions, and since the unholy book was in her hands as often as the holy one, she evidently suffered no pangs of conscience because her mind gave equal devotion to the escapades of the pagan gods and the words of the Hebrew prophets.

Hannah was probably one of the last of those little girls who were salvaged from orphan asylums and taken into homes to be trained as servants. She had been in my father's family in Glastonbury, a successor to "Aunt" Miranda, who had finally died there in the old Hale house after a long life of loving servitude, and who had been buried, as she knew she would be, in decency and with sincere mourners, in the family lot of her adopted people.

All prosperous New England houses knew the presence of such spinsters as these, and their life stories always seemed to be the same: years of selfless devotion, particularly to the growing children whom they thought of as their own, wholehearted loyalty to the roof that gave them shelter, and in the end, their own grave among all the others whose lives they had shared, with "Aunt So-and-so" carved on the headstone. Sometimes these women far outdid their families in pride and self-importance. Hannah, for one, felt that her household and herself as a part of it were so privileged that they were practically outside the law.

"Us Hales can do anything," she would say. "We're royalty, ain't we?"

She was about the same age as my father, and when he married and brought his bride back for their first visit together in Glastonbury, none of his sisters had eyes more watchful or more critical than Hannah's of all the new Mrs. Hale said, did, or wore. Once, coming home after a drive, my mother found Hannah in her room turning down the bed for the night. She finished her task and turned to go, but stopped at the door and said abruptly:

"I guess I might as well tell you—while you've been gone, I've tried on all your hats."

She stood there in the doorway, her bony hands clasped across her apron, her straight sandy hair slicked back from her brows and ears, her homely freckled face beaming with mischief. My mother burst out laughing.

"Well, Hannah," she said, "which one suits you best?"

Later, when my father chose to live in his wife's old home in Norwich Town rather than in Glastonbury, Hannah went along too. And so she sat that winter evening in 1893 waiting for Mrs. John Hale to have the last of her many children, and suffering with her in the keen way that simple natures do when they love the sufferer.

Hannah had been prophesying for some weeks now that this time Mrs. Hale would have a little girl. Unobtrusively, at odd moments all through the day she had been studying the changes in her mistress's figure and comparing them with former observations of other women who had been "on their way." Before this, the Hale babies had been boys, and during these former pregnancies Mis' Hale's shape had been "diffrunt." But this time, Hannah kept telling herself, this time, Mis' Hale's shape put her in mind of Ada Perkins, and Ada had always had girls. Yes, there were no two ways about it, this time Mis' Hale's shape was *just* like Ada's.

She was assuring herself of this for the thousandth time when she heard Mrs. Robinson's discreetly quickened steps in the hall outside the door of my grandfather's room, where he and my father were sitting together waiting—no doubt miserably enough. Hannah knew that at last the nurse had come down to announce that "things had begun in earnest."

Presently Fred was told to hitch up Charlie and drive

to the Doctor's, a mile away, to take the news. If he felt reluctant to leave the warm bright kitchen and the steaming kettle, he was soon consoled by the homely rhythm of the old horse's plodding feet mingled with the cheery sound of the sleigh bells, and far above him in the silent dark wheeled the glittering constellations which had companioned him on many a winter journey. Fred loved what he reverently called "the firmumunt." He said it always reminded him of verses from "Scriptur'," and these he softly whispered to himself as he jogged along, gently flapping the reins and every now and then squirting a stain into the roadside snow from his ever present quid.

Dr. Burton Palmer lived down in Norwich in one of the square imposing houses facing the park which surrounded the Soldier's Monument. At the time I was born he was a man in early middle age, with a broad ruddy face and genial high spirits. He was a bachelor whose house was presided over by a tall, handsome sister, and both of them enjoyed living in the grand manner. Dr. Palmer admired good food, pretty women, and thoroughbred horses. At one time he drove out to make his calls behind a three-horse team, the small, graceful sleigh gaily decorated with scarlet tassels and with silver bells that seemed to chime as sweetly as those in a clock. Patients pleaded eagerly to have their beds moved close to the window in order to be able to watch for the appearance of all that exciting lovely color, movement, and sound. The outfit dashed up the snowy road, the fur-clad Doctor looking like a Russian prince as he held the reins with easy skill in one hand while with the other he waved to everyone he passed—and of course he passed everyone.

His father too had been a doctor, physician to the older generations of all those families his son later served. When Dr. Palmer sat by your bedside he not only counted your own individual pulse, he remembered also the family heartbeat. To balance your own private fever, he would rely on decades of health which he realized had been enjoyed by your whole clan. In short, he knew every bone in the family skeleton as well as he did the texture of the flesh that covered it.

Perhaps this huge accumulation of intimate knowledge sometimes led him astray, into a too-careless confidence that certain circumstances would be repeated indefinitely and without variations, in the same patterns. He had already delivered other babies of my mother's—some living and some dead. He knew that childbirth for her was difficult and slow. No doubt remembrances of these former occasions returned to him when Fred at length arrived with his message. It is possible that he may have had a cigar or a bottle of port or an anecdote to finish. Certainly he was in no hurry to leave his comfortable chair and his library fire and drive off through the cold away out to Norwich Town for Judge Hoyt's daughter Mary, who would probably keep him up all night anyway. But for once Mary varied her usual procedure and gave the Doctor, as well as her household, a startling surprise.

During the long interval between Fred's departure and Dr. Palmer's arrival, the old house in Norwich Town was abustle with the excitement of receiving its new and apparently all-too-impatient guest. Mrs. Robinson was accustomed to the role of lieutenant, but hardly to that of general, and this insubordinate baby's refusal to wait for the presence of the commanding officer somewhat disconcerted her. Lacking the Doctor, she felt the need of any man—even a husband—and she called for my father. Stripping off his coat as he went, he ran up the stairs. His voice as he spoke to my mother was calm and quieting. He rolled up his sleeves, and with the competence that never seemed to fail him in any human crisis, he went to work.

So it was that when the Doctor's step eventually sounded outside on the icy walk, an upstairs window banged up sharply and my father's voice called out:

"Is that you, Burton? Well, my friend, the baby's here. You've lost your fee this time." Then they both laughed, and it always remained a joke between them.

My father had had many sons. Now, at the end, in his middle age, he had his daughter. The tenderness that he showed toward all his babies was intensified and deepened for her. Because of the richness of his nature, in any event the tie between them would have been close and warm. Now it held the added significance, to him very romantic and piercingly sweet, that his own hands had been the first to touch her, to hold her, to welcome her into life on earth.

He dreamed extravagant and loverlike and absurdly impossible dreams for this tiny person. Of course she would have all the features and the qualities that he most admired in women—a quiet voice, deft hands, height, and grace. She must love, as he did, the names of wild flowers, stormy days, swimming in the sea, the first star at dusk, and books and the music of old hymns. She must wear white a great deal both in summer and in winter. And when she was eighteen, he would give her a string of pearls!

My two brothers were not so wholehearted in their enthusiasm. Indeed, when first presented to me, Ned, just a year and a half my senior, frankly and contemptuously spat at me. Then he stamped over to his mother, who was smiling at him from the bed, and though his vocabulary was limited, showed her by unmistakable furious sounds and gestures that she was to get up at once and resume the familiar order of affairs, in which he had been so lately the center of all attention. Mrs. Robinson, standing by the bed, raised her eyebrows and pursed her lips primly.

"My, my, bad boy! Mustn't be jealous," she said.

Hannah, too, grinned, and pointed her finger at him amiably:

"Now, Mr. Ned, you ain't the baby in this family no more. Your nose is broke for sart'n."

Sam, the older brother, at first regarded me from a distance, but there was a wistful curiosity in his look. He was a gaunt, delicate child, who had spent some part of his ten years strapped in steel braces, which was the treatment then for a crooked spine. Already his face was old and sternly marked by patient suffering, but his eyes were still a child's, candid and hopeful. He had found Ned somewhat violent as a companion, but perhaps a little sister might prove a milder playmate. And he wanted so much to have other children around him and to be as nearly like them as he could. It must have seemed a long time now since he had known Lawrence, that other brother just two years younger than himself who had died, and he was tired of being alone. So after watching me,

Sam asked timidly if he might hold the new baby. Sitting, gravely responsible, in his small black chair, he was allowed to rock me gently for a short while.

To my grandfather I was just "another young one." Children had no interest for him until they could walk and talk and generally show some signs of being humanly companionable. Babies, he often remarked coarsely, always puked in his beard. And after all, it was his own beloved daughter who had had to endure giving me birth.

He must have been glad, that January night, when it was over. Left by himself, no doubt he fidgeted among his papers in his irritable way as he sat at his desk pretending to write. Or he may have bent his head, his eyes half-closed, strangely quiet for once as he remembered those other nights when his own children were born, when Elizabeth his wife, not Mary his daughter, had been the one to lie upstairs in that same room in that same agony. But when he went out into the hall to join my father and the Doctor, he was his usual brisk, unsentimental self, chaffing and joking with them and roaring for Hannah to bring something in for them all to eat and drink.

Half-resentful of those cheerful male voices, my mother closed her eyes wearily, still uncaring that the baby had proved to be a daughter and not another son. There had been so many babies, and birth had always seemed the same. Presently Mrs. Robinson, smiling her chilly, genteel smile, bent over the bed. The smell and the rustle of her clothes were reassuringly comfortable and clean; her placidly moving hands seemed somehow to restore order not only in the room but in the universe. But often, later, I was to hear my mother say of her daughter:

"She gave me less trouble coming than any of them did."

Trouble . . . trouble . . . I would repeat silently within my wondering mind. Why should my mother think that I would cause any trouble coming among these people, into this house, when she must know that I had chosen them myself for my very own?

CHAPTER II

THE BROTHERS

NED had declared war with me at that moment of our introduction as I lay in the cradle and he was held over me for a first look at his sister. Our childhood together, linked so closely because we were so near of an age, was an embattled one. We joined forces only against some powerful adult or against Sam, our older brother. Sometimes the two boys, in spite of being nine years apart, stood out against me at moments when they felt that too many and too enviable privileges were accorded me because of my position as "the only daughter." Then again, Sam and I, whose temperaments were subtly harmonized at some points, knew how to subdue Ned, though physically he was more than a match for both of us together.

But a general fracas, in which each fought individually against the other two—and probably also with some vague grudge against the whole world—was the instant when the quiet old house became illumined with a three-cornered flame that was hot, crackling, and well worth while. Such outbursts were the only times when we really all looked alike. The slight family resemblance that we bore to one another lay in the shape of our eyes and the heavily marked brows. When the dark eyebrows drew down at the same time over the three pairs of blazing eyes, we ceased to be Sam, Ned, and myself and rushed together into solid Hale, consumed in the fire of our common blood.

Once, when my mother told me that if all her babies had lived, I would have had nine brothers, I cried out: "Oh, what a blessing they didn't! What a perfect *blessing* for me!" And I often indulged in dreams of how peaceful life must be for one of those lucky creatures, always spoken of with such pity in the grown-up world, as an "only child."

Ned was tall, strong, handsome, and masterful. He got what he wanted not by any finesse, but by direct action and force of muscle. In those first years, he and I often sat facing one another in the same baby carriage. He would endure this tête-à-tête in a bored but amiable fashion if a guardian happened to be present, but once alone with me, he would turn into a ruffian. The bottle would be ruthlessly torn from my feebler grasp, and before my wails could summon help it would be completely emptied and cast aside. Ned would sit triumphantly smacking his lips, his lovely, clear-featured little face rosy from such strong gulping, his big gray eyes alight with wicked laughter, and the dimple in his left cheek delightfully displayed. As we all grew older, Sam and I often used that dimple to embarrass and humiliate Ned.

"Now show your dimple," we would sneer. "Just show your pretty, pretty dimple, and you'll get what you want."

Often my mother herself surrendered to its charm, but there were other times when even she seemed resentful of its power over people—particularly soft-hearted nurses and teachers.

"Well," she would observe in disgust after hearing of some victorious encounter of Ned's, "I suppose the dimple got in its work."

Sam too possessed strength and beauty, but of his own strange kind, not revealed often nor to everyone. Accustomed from the beginning to his frail, twisted figure, I accepted him quite naturally, and was friendly or quarrelsome in the same moody, sisterly fashion as with Ned. My mother and father spoke sadly, though seldom, of "Sam's trouble" or "Sam's affliction," but Ned and I did not speak of it at all, even to each other. There seemed to be always in each one of the family, both parents and children, some fiercely protective secret promise never to use, or even to think, the brutal word "hunchback." To Ned and me, Sam appeared only as the very much older brother, set apart by years and experience, which gave him the advantage always implicit in any older-brother status. We respected particularly his tongue, so gifted to dart a stinging taunt into our most vulnerable points; and in physical combat, even after the years when we topped him in height, the grip of his narrow hands was something to remember, to fear, and to avoid. In repose his face, even as a boy, was the bitterest one I have ever seen, but it was often transfigured by a smile of singular sweetness and charm.

I have always remembered the fall evening when I first actually realized how Sam differed from the rest of the world, how he was cruelly marked out as one not shaped like other people. I stood in the yard as he came out of the kitchen, leaving the door open behind him, and the light, streaming out across the driveway, cast his shadow on the side of the barn. In that dark reflection his long thin arms and legs, so out of proportion to the rest of his congested body, swung longer and more grotesquely awkward than ever, a kind of writhing tangle, spidery and malevolent. It was not the image of my brother as I thought of him. It seemed rather the image of some evil enchantment in which he was caught and held, a helpless and piteous prisoner. I had intended to call out to him, but instead I remained silent, standing there by myself in the night, my heart grieving and my mind full of fear.

He had learned early in his life to defend himself in his own indomitable way. If strangers on the street stared at him with insolence, he returned the stare—often stopping short in his path as he did so—with such a level gaze and so much contempt in the light-brown eyes under the heavy brows that it would be the stranger who turned away first, and with a look of shame. He hated scorn, but pity he hated even more savagely, because he feared it as well. He was still quite a little boy when my mother found him one day sobbing his heart out in his own room after a croquet game with some other children.

"They let me beat!" he cried. "They *let* me!"

It seemed as though from the very beginning Ned and I had sensed this particular passionate fear. We knew, without ever being told, that Sam, even more than the proudest of straight people, wanted no quarter given, and so we acted accordingly. With us he could lay aside his dwarf's shape and let his spirit spring up fair and radiant and tall. Not by any word or deed or even glance was he ever excluded from our battles or our games by being reminded that he was different from us. We ignored his misfortune with what must have often seemed to others the most complete hardheartedness, but by our doing so he gained what he so bitterly longed for and so seldom received, snatches of utter self-forgetfulness and the momentary illusion that he too fitted comfortably into the common human mold.

Both Ned and Sam took possession quite brutally of anything that was mine if it suited their purposes or struck their fancy. Ned used my little silver scissors to cut wire, and Sam dusted himself off after his bath with my powder puff, dipped in the scented powder in the ivory box my mother had given me. Ned stole my diary out of my desk, read it, and quoted it in public to my humiliation and distress.

But Sam's intrusions on my privacy were often of too friendly a nature to resent. Like my mother, he loved all that was dainty and fine—jewels, rich colors, perfumes, exquisite fabrics—though he was afraid of them all for his own use. He would walk through the garden touching the sweet peas, or leaning to draw in the sweetness of a dark-red rose. But if he picked a flower and put it in his buttonhole, he always took it out again before he left the house, for fear of doing something that would make him, as he said, "even more conspicuous."

When Sam was nineteen he went away to college, and during those years Ned and I were not of his superior world. Only during vacations he noticed us again, and not always to snub us, but often as though he wanted to know what we were up to these days, and to keep a share in it if he could. He came now and then into my room to perch on the window seat under one of the sunny front windows while I sat brushing and braiding my hair.

"Let me brush it. It looks just like molasses candy," he would say.

Before me, in the mirror, I would watch his gaunt, tired-looking face, which hung down between his mis-shapen shoulders so much lower than most faces do. His long arm moved awkwardly, but his hand was gentle, and in his eyes rested, for a moment, an expression of grave delight. Once, sitting so beside me after a silence in which I felt some specially intensified kind of watchfulness, he said softly and a little wistfully:

"I'm glad this happened to me and not to you. It would be much worse for a girl to look like this."

For an instant I did not know what he meant, and then as I realized sharply and painfully just what he had in mind by "this," I turned away in confusion, longing to be old enough to have learned what the words were—and I was so sure that there must be some—which would comfort him.

"Oh, no! It wouldn't," I finally stammered, staring down at my hands. "No, it wouldn't, Sam. It wouldn't have mattered at all."

But he only shook his head and repeated, almost as if to himself:

"Yes, it would. *I know.* It would have been a lot worse for a girl."

One of Sam's bravest achievements, and it must have been an early one, was the conquering of envy. To him was closed for always that whole radiant world of adventure and prowess where Ned could square his broad shoulders and swagger like a hero. Yet his admiration for his younger brother's skill and superiority in sports and games he kept unflawed by any sullen self-pity. More than any of us, he seemed to want and to urge Ned to be a fighter and a winner, and rejoiced in every sign or report of his strength and daring.

In addition to a body bursting with vitality, Ned's imagination housed some kind of personal daemon that prompted him to exploits which had an odd, almost mythological flavor. He was not content with any ordinary tests of force and endurance, but wanted and constantly sought the variety of danger that edged off sharply toward violent disaster. On this quest, which drew him over the whole countryside, he had one companion, a boy whom he called for no known reason "Beany." Beany was a small, spare, slightly bent boy, but tough as a piece of wire; his peaked face wore almost continuously a faint, sardonic smile. He paced at Ned's side, an inescapable shadow, no doubt quite capable of creative ideas himself but certainly always for Ned in his ventures an able second and a faithful aide.

All four elements were their playground, but among these water, with its infinite possibilities, drew them like a magnet. Beyond our house, over the hills to the east, lay a large solitary pond edged by thick woods. There, one day early in summer Ned's lunatic fancy conceived the idea of trying to swim across the widest expanse with his hands and feet tied. Beany obligingly and all-too-competently performed this office for his friend, then ran around to the other side to be ready to greet him when he should arrive victoriously, as they both seemed completely certain that he would.

Ned hopped down to the edge and plunged violently in. The quiet brown surface of the pond flashed and foamed under the convulsions of his hampered but determined young body. Toward the end, however, even Beany's superb confidence failed him, and he ran out into the deep water and dragged his half-drowned hero to safety. When they were both up on the bank, he stood breathing hard and staring down at Ned, who lay at his feet naked and still bound. After a few moments of agonized gasping, Ned spat out the last mouthful of pond and heaved himself up into a sitting position. Beany's wry smile reappeared on his thin face. "Cripes!" he remarked softly, and then they both collapsed into laughter.

In the spring, when the freshet in the river overflowed into the meadows just across the road from our house, the two boys could find plenty of excitement closer to home. If you stood on the iron bridge over that swollen black torrent, you could see the ice floes whirling down between the banks, jamming in the roots and overhanging branches of the trees, or crashing together in midstream with a shock that made the floor of the bridge tremble under your feet.

Such a scene was only one more ringing challenge to Ned and Beany. Each boy would catch and mount a slippery floe, ride it until the last instant before perilous collision, then escape, either by jumping for another cake of ice floating near by or for the riverbank itself, or by swinging up into the frozen branches of a tree. Each leap was punctuated by a loud triumphant yell. All up and down the meadows on those gray afternoons you could hear the excited voices mingled with the roaring of the river and the crash of the breaking ice.

But it was on the other, bigger river, the Shetucket, far across the town and beyond it, where Ned had what was perhaps his strangest encounter of all—that one with a swimming deer. He was there one early spring day in a canoe, and the deer, carried by the icy current, was swept close enough to stir Ned into one of his mad impulses. He laid down his paddle and shouted to the boy in the stern of the canoe:

"I'm going to ride him!"

But this time the other boy, unfortunately, was not the understanding Beany. He was older and warier, and he persuaded Ned to keep his seat.

"You can't catch him," he said disgustedly, "and even if you could, his hoofs would tear your legs to pieces."

Ned hesitated, staring and still longing—and so his chance was gone. The delicate, branched head, the gentle face with its wild, lovely eyes, drifted rapidly away, and Ned took up his paddle, deeply regretful and sulky.

When I heard about it, I felt queerly cheated myself. It seemed as though Ned had refused some really royal invitation—perhaps the only one he would ever have—to travel in an enchanted land. I believed that in choosing to stay safely in the boat rather than to leap and go, however doomed a rider, on that unearthly creature, he had made the wrong and somehow unforgivable decision. Now he would always be remembered as just another boy in Connecticut of whom the neighbors said:

"He'll come to no good end. You mark my words. That Hale boy will never, *never* come to any good end."

Because Sam was so much older, he could remember a whole part of the family life long before Ned and I had been born into it. We were always ready to hear him tell of those other days when my mother and father, in the early years of their marriage, had lived on Gramercy Square in New York, and my father's business had been something always romantically alluded to as the "Mexican Venture." This seemed to have been connected with a mine, but we remained contentedly vague about it, delighted mostly with the thought that Father had been to that remote, exotic land, and that his dreams as a young husband should have led him so far away from tiny old Connecticut.

Then too, there had been that other brother, Lawrence, two years younger than Sam, who unlike the other babies had lived at least long enough beyond infancy to remain for Sam a very real and lastingly clear memory. Of all that they had shared together, Ned and I liked most to hear of the family of white mice that had been their pets, and had increasingly overrun the rooms of the apartment.

Apparently the two little boys had played with the mice much as girls do with dolls, devising furniture and houses for them out of cardboard boxes and, most exciting of all, using them as passengers on their trains of cars, where the meek whiskered faces poked through the windows like very scared little old men. Indeed, whatever equipment those cars lacked could somehow be supplied by this resourceful pair, as my mother discovered when she found her diamond ring, lost for some time, hanging on the front of the small engine to serve as a headlight.

Perhaps death always lends some legendary quality to a child's remembrance, but certainly Lawrence's pictures showed a face of startling beauty with its golden hair and its enormous brown eyes. He had died just after the famous blizzard of '88, and my father had been one of the many frantic parents who tramped the deserted and drifted streets trying to get milk for his children, the quest in his case even more pathetic than most because he knew that one of his boys was dying. My father never spoke of Lawrence—perhaps he couldn't bear to—but my mother often did, her words always carrying the implication that, somewhere, this loveliest and most sensitive of her children bided his time, waiting for her to come.

Lawrence's death occurred in the same year as the collapse of the "Mexican Venture." My grandfather still remained, aging and alone, in the old house in Norwich Town, and my mother, grief-stricken now and left with only the one frail little oldest son, naturally turned to him. So the family returned there, and my father went into one of the banks of Norwich, but with the intention of staying only until some one of the splendid but shadowy schemes in his mind should shape itself into a reality and he would once more set out into the world to find at the end of a rainbow a fortune worthy of those he loved. The miracle of such an arch never materialized for him in any actual sky, certainly not in that of Connecticut, and the life of the house there closed in around him, drifting with him through the years.

In some ways the work at the bank suited and contented him, for he was a methodical man with the patient mind of a student. And if he rebelled at so quiet a destiny, it was with sadness rather than bitterness, as if he glimpsed in flashes, momentary and perhaps but dimly apprehended, that hidden deep within him lay sources of nobler power than he would ever call upon himself to use.

"Queer tribe, those Hales," an old man in Glastonbury used to say. "They just don't know their own strength."

He was thinking of their fists and what he had seen them do, once the slow Hale temper was aroused, startling themselves more than anyone else by the resultant devastation. Yet his comment, had he but known it, probed deeper than their muscles and their bones. And there ran, too, in some of that "queer tribe" a strain of mysticism which limned their figures with a faint but unforgettable poetry. Aunt Sophia Hale, one of the sisters, lived by this light and so, perhaps in a lesser degree, did my father. Linked closer than most people to Nature, they revered and accepted all her inscrutable ways much as primitives do, save that their worshipful wonder at her altars never seemed to be flawed by any fear.

My father had a calm way of walking out to watch a thunderstorm that my mother never quite forgave. Cowering somewhere with the shades drawn and her face hidden, she was irritated to think that he also did not run headlong, looking and praying for safety. Instead, he would stand on the open front porch, his hands in his pockets, marking every change in the piled clouds that charged across the sky, exulting in the fierce explosions of the thunder, loving the wind that whipped through the maple trees, bowing them down and filling them with a tumult that sounded like the sea. He would lift up his face into all that fire and light not as if he challenged it, but as if he shared it, a natural and necessary part of it, and no more afraid of its plunging into him than a sheath is afraid of the sword.

Occasionally this very serenity in the face of what most people dreaded and avoided would startle my mother more than vex her. Accustomed to her irascible, nervous little father, this quality of her husband's always remained outside her comprehension, commanding from her an admiration that was not unmixed with awe. She had, in particular, one story to tell of him that she never told, even after countless repetitions, without giving the impression that she still half wondered if she had not dreamed the whole occurrence.

At one time, in the house below ours on the River Road there lived a young woman who often passed our gate. She was a pale little person with downcast eyes, always accompanied by an older woman who walked close at her side with a sullen, watchful, almost threatening air. This companion the neighbors always spoke of as a "keeper," for the girl had mysterious periods of insanity, when her docility vanished and she became unmanageable.

One moonlit summer night, her madness dreadfully upon her, this girl appeared at our front door. When my father let her in, she fell at his feet, clinging to his knees and moaning. She was half-naked, dressed only in her nightgown, one shoulder of which had been torn away, and she was covered with stains of blood. Not far behind her, but panting and in a black rage because her charge had escaped her, pounded the big woman who was her attendant. She had a cane in her hand, and taking hold of the girl by her streaming hair, wrenched her away and started to beat her.

My mother had come running halfway down the staircase, and stood there transfixed with horror. She knew only a little of these people from the reports of others, but it was enough to make her afraid. And at this moment, seeing and hearing them there so unaccountably in the hallway of her own home, whatever pity she might have felt for the girl vanished before her own terror. My father finally managed to snatch the cane, and made the woman loosen her savage grip on the girl who then, still sobbing and crouched over like an animal, darted into the library. The woman confronted my father angrily, but the glare in her eyes faded before some steadier light in his own. Ashamed, she began to mutter explanations.

"You have to beat her," she said.

"No, you don't," he replied. "You leave her here for a while and I will bring her home."

"You'll never be able to make her come," the woman said stubbornly.

"She'll come. But first you take your stick and get out of this house."

He gave her the cane, and after standing uncertainly for a moment staring at him, she turned and went out. He stepped quietly into the library, and my mother could hear him talking in low tones until the girl's sobs finally ceased. When they came out into the hall, her hand was on his arm and she was gazing up into his face with the spellbound eyes of a child. He was looking down at her, smiling a little, and still speaking in that courteous, perfectly casual voice. Slowly and almost ceremoniously, as if he had been taking her out to dinner, he led her through the door and down the walk. Her bare feet pattered confidently beside him, and the moonlight fell through the maple trees in lustrous shafts across their tranquil figures.

Perhaps it was true, as the old man in Glastonbury said, that the Hales did not know their own strength. But others seemed to sense its presence, and to lean on it during trouble that was trivial as well as serious. Even my grandfather, that testy, independent old soul, relied on my father's serenity and patience many times. Grandfather had almost a genius for disorder, and often looked in vain for some suddenly necessary document in all that wild litter on his desk. It was there—he knew it—but some devil must be hiding it just to plague him, some dirty, invisible devil who couldn't invent enough mischief in hell and so sprang around on an old man's desk, snatching papers out of his very hand. He could work himself into a convulsion over such a small affair, and as his muttered discourse with the evil one increased in volume and profanity, my mother, fearing for the delicate ears of her children, would say hurriedly to her husband:

"Oh, please go in and see if you can straighten out Father!"

So in he would go and set to work in his deliberate fashion, his steady hands folding and arranging the papers, the petulant old man at his side fuming less and less as some semblance of order was restored. And when at last my father would hand him the desired sheets and say, "There you are, I think, Mr. Hoyt," the fiery blue eyes would glance toward the gentle brown ones and, somewhat shamefaced, he would murmur: "Bless you, John, bless you! You're a good fellow."

When my grandfather died, Ned and I were still small children, and so we did not have as much time in which to win his interest and his companionship as Sam did. Yet even with my small store of remembrances, as I think of the few years that we all lived together—the three generations under the same roof—he is the one, that slight, unconquerable figure with its aura of age and achievement, who stands out for me quite clearly as dominating our entire family group.

CHAPTER III

THE DOWNSTAIRS BEDROOM

AFTER my grandmother died, my grandfather always occupied the downstairs bedroom, and it was spacious enough to serve him as a study as well as a sleeping-room. Almost all New England houses had a bedroom on the first floor, sometimes called the parlor bedroom, sometimes the downstairs bedroom. Often, in addition, it was the spare room, used only for guests.

In our house, the downstairs bedroom was at the end of the hall behind the parlor, a large room with one window opening into the back yard and two facing the drive at the north side of the house, with a pleasant view through the trunks of the trees across Miss Bateman's lawn up the street. One door opened into it from the hall, and another led out into a long, cold storeroom with a door at the end, from which two steps led down into an open arched passage with a stone floor that connected the house with the woodshed.

A tall mahogany secretary with glass doors in the top that were divided into diamond-shaped panes stood between the two windows. There were bookcases near at hand in the corner, and also the "whirligig," a wooden stand of open shelves revolving on a central standard, which held more books and papers. In another corner, by the one window at the back, stood the washstand with pitcher and bowl, and against the wall at that end of the room, the massive Victorian bed with the huge, ugly walnut headboard.

My grandfather always used a Windsor armchair at his secretary, and in front of the fireplace, with the black-marble clock on the mantel, were grouped other big chairs of the ample, stuffed type and a rocker, all of them a little shabby from hours of comfortable ease. In winter a big iron stove stood on the hearth, its isinglass doors fiery and glowing, its black sides radiating enough heat to warm every part of the room except the space near the storeroom door, which was always a trifle draughty.

To that downstairs bedroom came not only the family and friends and legal associates, but occasionally some odd and rather startling guests. At that time my mother was an unmarried woman still quite contentedly close enough to girlhood to be spoken of as "a daughter in her father's house," a designation which implied dignity and some maturity, but not yet a position of hopeless spinsterhood.

Once, late at night, she heard from her bed upstairs unusual sounds in the hall below, steps pacing back and forth, voices speaking in undertones. Wondering uneasily whether "Father is all right," she pulled on her dressing-gown and went to stand unseen in the dimness at the head of the stairs. Below her, she watched her father and a man strange to her—who, she learned next day, was a well-known thief—going through the motions of a curious little performance. My grandfather had doubted the testimony of some witnesses as to the possibility of a man's watch being spirited away out of his pocket by fingers so agile that the man could remain completely unconscious of his loss. So this expert had been called in to give a private and professional demonstration of pocket-picking.

Here too came Mrs. Crawford, the Norwich Town woman accused of poisoning her husband by slipping arsenic into his breakfast coffee daily until her purpose was accomplished. In those days of his criminal-law practice, my grandfather defended all sorts of supposed malefactors, but he never did so unless he had some assurance of their innocence. He led her into his downstairs bedroom, seated her politely in the rocker by the stove while he paced the quiet room for a moment, his hands behind his back. Then he faced her, and with full recognition of the histrionic element in his appeal, no doubt, said harshly:

"Now, Mrs. Crawford, there is no one in this room but you and I and God Almighty. Are you a guilty woman, or are you innocent?"

Unquivering, she looked him squarely in his blazing blue eyes as she raised her hand.

"Mr. Hoyt," she replied, "before God Almighty, I am innocent."

God Almighty was a name often invoked by my grandfather in as many ways as he had emotions. If out of temper with the weather—and he always was the instant he saw the rain start to drip or the snow to fall—he would work himself up into an absurd but perfectly genuine passion and standing at the door or a window, his face purple and his clenched fists waving above his head, he would explode with "Any goddam nigger could run this universe better than God Almighty!"

But if the weather was fine and he felt fit and things were going his way, then his exuberant high spirits would allow him to be on better terms with his Maker. Such a moment occurred one morning in court when he was opposed by two lawyers named Jeremiah Lathrop and Solomon Brewer, whose arguments were long, dreary, and pompous. When at last they were done, he rose quickly to his feet and turned to the jury with a wicked spark in his eyes.

"Gentlemen," he remarked, "you have just listened to the lamentations of Jeremiah and the wisdom of Solomon. Now prepare to hear the Lord God Almighty."

There were many sides to his nature, elements as contradictory as his love of fine china and his delight in coarse anecdotes. As a younger man he had had literary ambitions, like almost everyone else in Connecticut. He preserved one of his printed pieces that had appeared, together with the offerings of others, in a small green volume called

The Moss Rose. Most of the contributions were in verse, but his was a prose piece, a highfaluting medieval romance with the title "Clarence de Courcy." The style and the sentiments were in complete contrast to his racy, cynical, and often profane conversation.

All women interested and attracted him, but he had a special admiration for the intellectual woman, seeking out such "literary ladies" in Connecticut as Lydia Huntley Sigourney, "the poetess," and Miss Perkins, who wrote historical sketches. Perhaps this was because of his mother, Felicity, who like many other eighteenth-century ladies believed in "the improvement of the mind," and who wrote and received very lengthy letters. On the other hand, he often burst out in praise of some matron as "a great, splendid, double-breasted, flat-bottomed creature," a vigorous phrase that was scarcely suggestive of a mental type.

Elizabeth his wife and his daughter Mary were certainly not literary, and also neither bore any resemblance to the Amazonian warrior suggested by his description of another kind of woman. But evidently Mary's companionship sufficed after Elizabeth's death, for he never remarried. If Mary lacked bookishness, she shared his keen appreciation of personalities, and both possessed to an astonishing degree the power of charming and managing people. But in this respect their natures, if alike, also diverged, for his democratic tastes led him anywhere and everywhere, while Mary, like her Grandmother Felicity, had many of the characteristics of a snob. This she knew, and even admitted with considerable pride.

"If I had money enough," she would say with that arrogant lifting of her lovely head, "I would be a complete snob."

The wealthy aristocrats and the humble working people of her time she understood and accepted, but between those two extremes, in that wide expanse of the commonplace which abounded in so much smugness, pretentiousness, and false gentility, she moved with complete and cold disdain.

My grandfather swallowed life whole, with both palate and digestion strong enough to savor and assimilate the entire mixture of ingredients. He watched and welcomed with tireless interest the changes in his town, his state, and his nation. That shrewd vision of his—sharpened and amplified by insight—reached back practically into the eighteenth century, and he looked forward farther and with more tolerance than most of his generation.

During his long lifetime he saw the Irish pouring into Connecticut in great numbers, and they were a people in whom he had faith and whom he understood. He used to boast that he could remember the day when there had been *the* Irishman in Norwich, and people went to inspect him as though he were a singular kind of beast. But that first bizarre specimen swiftly multiplied into hordes. They were then the hodcarriers, the ditch-diggers, and the servants. Illiterate, uncouth, the men passed the house swinging their black lunchboxes, smoking their vile-smelling stubby pipes, enlivening the streets with their rich voices and their incomprehensible speech, which somehow always rose and fell with the rhythms of poetry. Standing waist-deep in ditches by the roadside, they lifted those droll faces with the small, sharp eyes and the immensely long upper lips, grinning and spitting, as queer as leprechauns in this sedate Yankee town.

My grandfather lived to see them dig themselves out of the ditches to walk abreast with the descendants of the earliest settlers, their children and their grandchildren become dressmakers, contractors, lawyers, and businessmen. The brogue disappeared and the comical facial contours softened and sobered, but the coarse and fiery strength remained to be poured into restless ambition that drove them everywhere. And fire and coarseness and restless ambition were the very core of my grandfather's own heart.

However, this interest and admiration of his were not shared by his family. His wife, being English, had her own views, and his son, even as a small boy, referred to the Irishmen that came to the house as "those Greek friends of Father's." His daughter Mary laughed at them and imitated their burring speech to perfection, but she never went into the kitchen, as her father did, to sit down in the evening by the stove and exchange old wives' tales with whatever "Biddy" happened at the moment to be their cook.

My grandfather's memory ranged back a long way into the history of his country. Felicity had told him vivid tales of the Revolution, and he himself remembered dimly, as a tiny child, the War of 1812. The Civil War had taken his only son, Philip, and just how deeply that blow struck into him he never wholly confided to anyone. But unlike his wife, he did not allow it to kill him. Somehow he made peace with his own heart, and went on as eagerly as ever with his energetic life.

He wanted more than anything to be governor of his state, to stand at the head of his well-loved "old Connecticut." That honor, he felt, would set the perfect seal on both his youthful dreams and his manhood's labor. And he also often expressed the wish to live to be a hundred, to see the turn of his own century. But he did not realize either ambition.

He lay almost two years in that wide walnut bed in the downstairs bedroom, slipping away from earth very quietly and gently for one who had lived with such fierce activity. But his family was around him. Even Ned and I had been born, and my mother nursed him, caring for the frail old man as tenderly and as conscientiously as she had for her babies when they were small and helpless. He wanted no one near him but her, but her he wanted almost constantly, ringing for her, wherever she might be at her other tasks in the house, with a big brass bell kept on a table at his bedside. Her patient devotion seemed inexhaustible, and often as she came to him to bathe or rub or merely soothe him he would say to her, as he had said so many times during the long years: "Mary, you're one woman in ten thousand."

Lying there in the downstairs bedroom, he was far less remote and lonely than he would have been anywhere else in the house. So close to the kitchen, the woodshed, and the driveway, he could listen to all the small, important household noises—tradesmen coming and going, Hannah bustling in the kitchen, the calls and laughter of his grandchildren, Mary's quick steps just outside in the hall, or up and down the stairs. Winter days the azure coals would hiss softly in the big stove, and out on the road he could hear the bells on the sleighs sweetly ringing as they passed, or the slow wheels of carts wincing over the packed snow. Summer evenings with the windows open, the light breeze in the deepening twilight stirred the leaves in the maple trees—those trees he had planted so long ago. Tall now, and wide-spreading, they bent down around his house, and the low, rippling notes of the robins settling down for the night seemed very close to him, and silver-clear.

Before his increasing feebleness had forced him into bed, he had liked to sit on the small front stoop those summer evenings and watch the people passing on bicycles, curious "newfangled contraptions" that were ridden not only by men but—astonishing sight even without bloomers—by women too. He always counted them, and when he went in for the night told the number to his daughter. "Well, Mary, I counted fifty-seven tonight." What a world! If he only knew, if he only could wait to see and hear and share its destiny—all its destinies.

After he went to bed, he spoke less and less. He who had been so voluble, whose words had been dramatized with such imagination and variety by his mobile face and the gestures of the small, shapely hands of which he had been so proud, now lapsed into silence. Only once in a while his spirit flickered up in some momentary reminder of its former bright flare.

One day I passed through his room on my way to play in the woodshed. He did not object now if my brothers and I went in and out. His desk, where he had so hated interruptions, was closed forever, and the papers on the whirligig lay neat and undisturbed. I was a pudgy little girl by this time, with legs rounding out under my starched gingham dress and two braids of flaxen hair bobbing at my shoulders. My mother, sitting by his bed stirring a glass of medicine, watched the old man's gaze as it followed me across the room and through the door. For a brief instant, in those fading eyes she caught a ghostly glimmer of the old sparkle. She said quickly, bending toward him:

"What are you thinking about, Father?"

Very slowly he replied in the hoarse whisper which was all that remained of his voice:

"I was . . . just thinking . . . possibly . . . some day . . . that *That*"—he nodded in the direction I had taken—"might make . . . a very showy woman."

Occasionally Dr. Terence Devine stopped in to see him, more to make a social call than a professional one, for there was nothing he could do except to make suggestions for the old man's comfort. It was characteristic of my grandfather to prefer this sandy-haired, hard-bitten Irishman to the elegant Dr. Burton Palmer. No two could have shown greater contrasts, either as physicians or as men: one with all his rich inheritance, both of blood and of culture, his worldliness, his expansive geniality, his extravagant and luxurious tastes, his shining carriages and lively horses; the other a humble man straight from "the ould sod" who had had to fight every inch of his way for livelihood, for education, for practice, a brusque, shabby man who always sat a little forward in his dilapidated buggy as if he strained to overtake his old horse himself, his deep-set eyes gleaming under the greasy cap that he jammed down on his tousled head any way it happened to fall. But outside his medical training, which must have been meager, he had an earthiness, a warming humor, and a canny wisdom that were tonic.

It was he who on the summer afternoon that my grandfather died sat on one side of the bed while my mother sat on the other. Both realized that the old man lingering so long had reached the end at last. He himself knew it too, though he gazed up into their sad eyes quietly enough. But even then his daughter could not bear to let him go, clinging to his hand, trying to hold him back just a little longer.

"Speak to me," she begged. "Oh, Father, won't you say something to me?"

He stirred a little on his pillow, recalled briefly by that pitiful and urgent cry. Both Mary and the Doctor leaned close to him, watching those lips that hardly moved, waiting to catch up into their hearts—in that strange way that the living have—those last words spoken in the human voice by one so soon to be still, and which always keep so sorrowful yet so special a value.

What did they hope or expect to hear, those two beside the old man—his faithful physician and friend, his loyal, loving daughter? What echo now out of that long life of service and struggle, what faint return of his once gay, charming, and audacious self? He had for them no more than a humble whisper—it was what any tired child might have said as he turned his face to sleep at the end of the day.

"I've always . . . tried . . . to do . . . what was right."

CHAPTER IV

CORNER BISCUITS

FOR a few years after my grandfather's death, strangers being driven around the town were still shown our house as the residence of a leading citizen. If I happened to be playing around the front gate or on the bank under the linden tree, I would see the driver from one of the Norwich livery stables gesture with his whip as he said, "That's Judge Hoyt's place," and then, in a low mumble, he would tell the history of my grandfather's life. But after a time, particularly when my mother and father, with the aid of additions and repairs on the old house, had managed in an astonishing manner to change its whole look, it became known locally as "Hale's."

My grandfather did not leave a fortune, as he was not one of the well-known thrifty Yankee type, but he had managed to save enough so that the amount inspired his daughter and son-in-law to indulge their own highly developed talents for tasteful spending. It never occurred to either of them that now had come the blessed chance to pay off their debts, which had steadily mounted since their marriage, and to begin afresh with chastened hearts and a nest egg for the future. Both loved the old house and longed to fashion it more to their own ideas and needs. For some time before my grandfather's death they had discussed their plans with ever increasing enthusiasm and delight. Often late in the evening, when he came to bid them good night, standing in the doorway of the room upstairs which they used for their own sitting-room and looking in on them with an air of mingled admiration and disgust, he would remark:

"How on earth you two can find so much to say to one another after all these years of married life! God Almighty, I've heard your voices up here all evening."

In the beginning, my father's visions of the new home that must arise within and around the structure of the old one were far simpler than my mother's, but both of them lost their heads more than a little when they fell into the clever hands of the handsome young architect from New York. He was a dashing fellow, fresh from Paris, whence he had returned to his own country elegantly decorated with a brown beard and an exquisite accent, and bringing with him all the vicious architectural ideas of the time—bay windows, stained glass, oak staircases, colored tiles, and the rest. Almost immediately he must have surmised the helpless and charming innocence of the two dreamers with whom he had to deal, and he soon bombarded them with a collection of blueprints that I am sure meant less than nothing to my mother and not much more to my father.

When the actual work began, this man, attired in a suit of spotless white overalls, came on to superintend it. I followed constantly at his heels, for I had never seen or even imagined anyone like him. Also I harbored, secretly but tenaciously, a vague conviction that he ought to be watched. It seemed to me that the house must be in distress, having its entrails torn out, its head uncovered, and even its bones disturbed.

From the very first moment when I had stood alone in the driveway and had seen two men climb up to the roof on ladders and start pulling off the shingles, I had felt a peculiar bewilderment, and wondered why the wood and stone did not cry out in piercing tones of protest and indignation. To see whole rooms that I had known and loved go down into dirty confusion, and the staircase disappear entirely, stirred me to a dismal kind of heartsickness. Fearful lest this bearded stranger would wrest apart and completely demolish what had been the very dimensions of my life, I dogged his footsteps and hung on his every oddly pronounced word.

Perhaps he had some comprehension of my uneasiness, for he was very patient and gentle with me, sometimes taking me a little into his confidence about what was being done. Later, when the reconstruction became more clearly outlined and I could tell that home would remain, even if somewhat in disguise, I grew to like him, and at the last could even bear the way he tweaked my pigtails or cracked jokes about my striped stockings—with stripes that ran around my legs instead of up and down—without too much resentment.

While all this was in progress the family went to board for the summer with Mrs. Ellen Richards in her square white house overlooking the Norwich Town Green. This lady, whom we children were taught to call "Aunty Richards," had been a childless widow, more or less indigent, for many years. She was slender, erect, with snow-white hair, a placid, rather stony face, and a precise way of speaking. Aunty Richards did not share my mother's recklessness in household matters. There were not the same towering and apparently inexhaustible supplies of sheets, towels, blankets, napkins and tablecloths, nor were the helpings at the table so carelessly generous. We never went hungry, but the meals seemed to be definitely outlines, instead of running over at all the edges in the lavish way that they did at home.

One evening at supper we had a platter of biscuits, and as it was passed Sam, Ned, and I began to look for what we called the "corner biscuits." These were the ones from the corners of the pan, and had two deliciously crisp brown crusty sides instead of one. By the time the platter reached me there were none of these delectables left. I looked at my mother pleadingly, feeling that surely she could do something about this for me.

"The corner biscuits are all gone," I said mournfully.

"Yes, they seem to be," remarked my mother with a smile of slightly disdainful amusement. From the head of the table came the icily serene tones of Aunty Richards.

"Can't all have corner biscuits," she said with something of an air of reproof.

It was on the tip of my tongue to retort that we always did at home, but a warning glance from my mother prevented me. I would have spoken only the truth. Just how many pans of biscuits were always baked in the Hale kitchen in order that everyone could have a corner biscuit or two if he wished, or what became of all the softer variety in the centers, which must so often have remained in quantity, I never happened to notice. No doubt my mother never noticed either or if she did, ignored the waste, feeling it perfectly justified, since it occurred in the course of her children's desires. In her mind whatever we wanted we deserved to have.

"You spoil your children, Mary," Aunty Richards once remarked reproachfully.

"Do I?" replied my mother in a dangerously affable manner. "Well, they're *my* children. If I choose to spoil them that's my own affair."

Naturally such a philosophy of parenthood, so defiantly stated, was not within the comprehension of the Aunty Richardses, nor for that matter of anyone else except my father. "The best is none too good," was an axiom always repeated when either of my parents set forth to make some purchase or carry out some plan for their home or their children. My father had his moments of horrified revelation when he could foretell the disastrous results of such princely tastes, no matter how enthusiastically he shared them. Occasionally he tried to remonstrate, both with himself and with my mother, by showing in actual figures the woeful direction in which their finances were headed.

But my mother had spent her girlhood with an indulgent and adoring father. Over and over she had heard that "nothing is too good for Mary." She had always had "the best," and having it had brought her to no calamity in the end. The ruinous figuring made no impression on a mind that stood solidly unshaken in its naïve confidence that some god existed dedicated to eternal beneficence toward the Hale family. Did not her children's veins run with the blood of two of the oldest families in Connecticut? Certainly the best was none too good for them, and corner biscuits they should have, hot from the oven and running with butter, world without end.

Autumn came before we left Aunty Richards and returned home. Late one afternoon we went down to the finished house to spend our first night there. Yellow leaves from the maples were fluttering down across the lawn, and beyond the black iron bridge that spanned the river in the darkening meadows the sunset streaked the sky with chilly stains of apricot and gold. I watched it fade through the two front windows of the room that was now to be all my own. Then I turned back to take my first lesson in lighting a gas jet. Before, we had always had oil lamps and candles, so now I watched with great seriousness while the little yellow flames with blue centers spurted into sight on each side of my mirror.

The whole room was very fresh and dainty, with pink-

and-white-flowered cretonne on the walls instead of paper, and a hearth of pale-blue tiles under the white mantelpiece. I had been given my Great-grandmother Felicity's small cherry dresser with the curved front, and her long mirror in its gold frame with a row of little gold balls across the top. For some reason too, instead of either of my brothers I had my Uncle Philip's bed, the one with the four rounded posts. As I crept into it on that first night while my mother turned out the gas with an almost earnest care, I lay quietly awake in this new dark.

The sense of all those familiar objects around me which had belonged to my own people comforted me, and softened my sharp awareness of new sounds, and most especially of a new smell. This dark smelled different from the old, and my nostrils quivered like a small animal's as they acquainted themselves with its rough texture of fresh paint, green wood, and crisp curtains. It was not for some time that the odor of the house itself, of the old beams, walls, and rafters, penetrated again this superimposed layer of novelties, and I knew once more that faint mustiness, particularly on damp days, which is the very breath of ancient buildings, and which was the essence of my early childhood.

The difference in the night sounds did not appear so quickly. The only one on that first night which made itself known immediately was the tick of the tall new clock at the foot of the stairs, and every fifteen minutes its clear, delicate chime, ending on the hour with strokes of slow and solemn profundity.

With their usual waywardness in practical matters, my mother and father had bought this clock late in the summer, on an expedition to New York. Their intention when they left had been to buy rugs, which they now sorely needed in the wider spaces of the changed house, but once their eyes fell on the clock, their necessities were forgotten and only this luxury was remembered and desired. It had a big round silver pendulum engraved with my mother's initials. As I sat at my place in the dining-room, which had once been the downstairs bedroom, and looked across the new wide end of the hall, that pendulum on every swing caught the light on its shining surface so that, for an instant, a star seemed to quiver there. Often I forgot what was on my plate at mealtime, and I would lean sideways to whisper with the passing seconds, "My moth-er's star . . . my moth-er's star . . ."

The new sounds affected us all somewhat. Many times now late at night, my mother would wake my father, certain that she heard someone moving about downstairs. He never waited to light the gas but, leaping out of bed, would reach for the iron poker and with that in his hand march through all the rooms in the dark. I think it disappointed him never to meet an enemy. He was the head of the household now; the home seemed really his own. There lay his children, calling out sleepily from their rooms at the sound of his firm steps, and his alarmed wife, waiting for something dreadful to happen. The necessity to defend his own family with his own strength would have been very sweet. But it never came, and his fearless prowlings provoked nothing more than laughter and jokes next morning at the breakfast table.

Gradually we learned to recognize these various rustlings and clicks, and either slept through them or waited for them to come at their appointed moments, which some of them punctually did. My mother claimed that about one o'clock someone in starched skirts always climbed the stairs and set down a basket on the top step. It seemed to be heavy, and she could hear it creak. If we were not chattering too much at the supper table, we could not miss that footless step which invariably crossed the hall in front of the tall clock, came toward the dining-room as if to join us, then turned abruptly and went out, presumably by the front door. Sam would grin and say, "There goes the Sixth Member of the household," but Ned would snort with disgust and, letting out his belt a notch over his already well-lined stomach, pass his plate for another huge helping of roast beef and Yorkshire pudding, to stow it away with deep sighs of contentment.

I spent many happy minutes by myself wandering through the house that had been, as my mother always explained, "made over." Even some of the furniture and the pictures that I already knew from long acquaintance looked different now that they were set or hung in new places. There was one room at the front of the house across from the longer library where I went sometimes when the afternoon light poured in and the house was very still. This which once had been the usual prim New England parlor my mother's taste had transformed into a kind of small formal drawing-room. In its exquisite austerity—all gold and white and crystal—softened here and there by splashes of some warmer but still delicate color, it suggested in every detail the personality of the woman who had planned it.

I would tiptoe in there, carefully avoiding the tables

with their slender, tapering legs and the straight mahogany chairs, and make my way across to the small stand under the side window. There rested a rosewood music box that tinkled out four or five tunes with a gentle, pretty mournfulness. While I listened, I would stare at the design of golden fleurs-de-lis on the wall paper above the white paneling, and at the pattern of pale-pink tulips on the big gold-satin armchair where no one ever dared to sit, which was just at the side of the yellow-tiled fireplace where no one ever dreamed of building a fire. It was a beautiful little room, suitable for absolutely no useful purpose but delightful and amusing, and somehow valuable to us all.

Early that fall, after we were settled down in the house, all the friends and acquaintances, not to mention the enemies who were hopeful for a chance to belittle and deride, arrived to have a look at what John and Mary Hale had "done" to the old Hoyt place. Probably it was during those calls, and the inevitable tours of inspection, that I began to learn by heart all the family tales and legends. Tagging along through the rooms as my mother led around a bevy of white-gloved ladies, I heard retold again and again all those fragments of lore which had attached themselves through the years to each object belonging to someone who had belonged to me.

In a corner cupboard, on wide shelves behind a glass-paned door, were Alcock and Wedgwood pitchers, their pale lavender and blue sides decorated with white classical figures, and a set of curious octagonal plates, in their centers pictures of red deer standing startled amid a sparse spring landscape. Those had been treasured by Elizabeth

Hoyt, my English grandmother, and in the hall hung the portrait of her son Philip, in his dark-blue Civil War uniform. There was a whole panel of miniatures, gentlemen in stocks and ladies in caps and fichus of frailest muslin. Two of these were always provocatively introduced by my mother as "the youth who vanished in the swamps of Florida" and "the little daughter of Tracy's first wife, who died of yellow fever in New London."

Tracy Hoyt had had three wives, the last one being Felicity. Near her portrait hung his, not painted as hers was in forbidding old age, but as a young man in a ruffled neckcloth, one arm resting on a desk and beside it a tall quill pen. Tracy's florid face looked out at you humorously, and a little shrewdly, as if he meant to enjoy all the good things of life and not pay too dearly for them. In an arched niche at the back of the library mantelpiece stood a big green jar of Chinese porcelain. Even without the story my mother could tell about it it would have been interesting and beautiful, with its soft colors, its design of dragons and wreathed flowers, and the squat, mythical beast—something like a toad with a beaded crown—that served as a handle for its cover. It had been Tracy's, and twice, packed with pieces of family silver, he had buried it in his garden in New London, first during the Revolution when the British burned the town, and again in 1813 when the townsfolk thought the British were about to repeat their destruction. In front of the jar on the mantel lay the powderhorn that had been carried by Dr. Jonathan Adgate, Felicity's father, during the French and Indian War in Canada.

So it was that many an afternoon, as I walked solemnly

after my mother and the exclaiming ladies in their rustling finery, I walked also on a road of my own imagining, back into the lives of all these people behind me, my own blood, far back through the years and even the centuries, absorbed and happy. My mother's stories gave me the key into a world where I could play my own endless game of conjecture and discovery. Ned never joined me in this game. He was too busy out in the fields and woods, he and Beany, graduating from mere explorers and experimenters into the skillful and predatory handlers of traps, rods, and guns. But Sam became my valuable companion in the past. He knew what I was after and followed whatever way I took, enlivening my imaginary journeys with good jolts of irreverent truth that were very salutary for his dreamy, sentimental sister.

Between Sam's realism and my own romanticism we reconstructed, little by little, the characters that were suggested by my mother's inherited anecdotes about the pictures and other objects in the rooms around us, and which were amplified by the old letters and books in the attic. Dr. Jonathan Adgate, Felicity, Tracy Hoyt and his first two wives and their children, my Grandfather Turner, his English wife Elizabeth and their son Philip—we stretched out our hands and drew them all out from the shadows. If I had opened so many graves by myself, I might have developed into nothing but a sickly moonstruck little ghoul. But Sam taught me to dig in the sunlight, so that the mold crumbled and dried and fell away from me, leaving no noticeable stain.

CHAPTER V

THE HOUSE

OUR house, so valiantly brought up to date by my parents, was built in 1761 by a sea captain. My grandfather bought it in 1842 shortly after his marriage to Elizabeth Dodd. By that time he was prospering as a young lawyer, and wanted a home not only for his bride but also for his mother Felicity, then an aged woman; the sea captain's house in the older settlement known as Norwich Town was not far from the one where Felicity had been born and had lived as a little girl.

In the earliest times Norwich City—what eventually became the business section as well as the wharves on the water front—was called Chelsea, or the Landing. It developed only slowly, because there were other trading centers farther down the Thames River. (We were always taught to pronounce this Temz, after the way of old England, and Norwich, Norridge.) The river's course commenced at the Landing, where two smaller streams, the Yantic and the Shetucket, flowed together. Before the forests were cleared the whole area was wild and marshy, and often deeply flooded in the spring.

For some time the real activities of the first settlers—the shops, the tavern, and the meetinghouse—were at Norwich Town, two miles up the Yantic. Very much later the distance between these two sections gradually filled up with houses of variegated Victorian architecture. The most pretentious of these were on Washington Street and Broadway, two wide shady streets running parallel to each other, which converged at the Civil War Soldier's Monument and made North Washington Street. This in its turn divided farther on, the left-hand way becoming River Road, where our house stood just a short distance below the Norwich Town Green.

Eventually the people in Norwich Town became a little smug in their attitude toward those who lived in Norwich City. They felt themselves to be more "established," more of the older order. Sometimes this air of superiority led them into amusing and embarrassing mistakes. There was, for instance, that unhappy guess made by Mr. Cyrus Loomis, a boastful man, who lived in the oldest house of all. Cyrus decided to carve the date when it was built over the front door, never condescending to verify it. Others did, however, and gleefully hastened to tell him that the date he had selected was about two decades previous to the settlement of the town, and could not possibly have been claimed by anyone unless by an Indian for his wigwam.

If Norwich Town regarded Norwich City with a patronizing eye, the city, on the other hand, disapproved severely of the town, because by reason of its insistence on separateness there were two sets of taxes, as well as other difficulties as to fire and police protection constantly presenting themselves.

Before the sea captain built our house in 1761, Norwich Town already had behind it a century of history in which, from the beginning, some of Felicity's people had taken part. She never forgot her pride in this, and she kept green especially the memory of that original settler, a man who had been the younger son of a nobleman. Because of a better education than most, this man easily assumed and maintained a place of leadership in the young colony. He had many sons, strong young men, gathered around him long before he was too old himself to command them, and they rooted themselves into this new earth with tenacity and strength. He never returned home, and none of his descendants saw England, nor did Felicity. And even though the two wars, the Revolution and that of 1812, occurred in the course of her lifetime, she still kept, separately hoarded, a strong sentiment of loyalty for her dream of that faraway island where she felt that her people had been gentlefolk.

This arrogant woman with so deep a passion for the past turned toward the future also, and with no small eagerness and hope, in the person of her only child, her son Turner. But he was often her vexation as well as her pride. He could not always be so serious as she about those ancestral shadows. He respected his mother's fierce devotion to gentility, and her tireless efforts to maintain something like a decent and graceful way of life even in the days of their poverty, but he felt too that he was a young man, alive in his own world, and that he had, as the saying was, "other fish to fry." He had a pliable, democratic nature; hers was stiff and aristocratic. Nor was there much in his vivacious face and small, quick person to suggest the stately woman in that portrait of her, painted in undaunted old age, which reveals so clearly by the dignity of the head in its staid, white bonnet tied precisely under the chin why she had been known in Norwich Town as "the Lady Hoyt."

Our house on the River Road was originally the simple white New England type with one central chimney, straight stairs just inside the front door, and a square room on each side of the hall as you entered. The years with their different demands, fashions, and tastes brought changes to this first austere design, but even in 1900, when it suffered its most elaborate disfigurements—a semicircular porch with two tall Doric columns, Southern-mansion style, plate-glass windows, and a front door of solid oak—even then it somehow managed to retain its essential outline of satisfying proportions and its atmosphere of sturdy dignity.

There was a short lawn that sloped slightly toward the inevitable white fence, and across the road, beneath a walled embankment, low-lying meadows stretched level to the Yantic flowing in its narrow channel between slanting trees and overhanging thickets. Beyond the meadows, on the other side, was a shallow wood growing on a steep hillside and partially concealing the Central Vermont Railroad tracks. In seasons when the foliage was thin there were two breaks in that wood through which the rushing, clangorous little trains were visible from our front gate. There were only a few of these a day, the most exciting one in the early dusk, when we sometimes caught a glimpse of the fireman standing in a rosy flare flinging coal into the open mouth of his hungry monster as the train gathered speed for the upgrade on the way to Bean Hill and Yantic, the villages just above us.

My brother Ned and I had a nurse named Mamie Brady, a blue-eyed Irish girl beloved by one of the Central Vermont brakemen. He used to wave at her from the train as it passed those openings in the wood, and she, a handkerchief in her hand, would wave back while we children stood beside her at the front gate. Later he became the baggage-master down in the Norwich station, and whenever trunks were to be checked Ned and I always trailed after the grown-ups to speak to "Mamie's beau." Even after the baggage-master had grown gray and a little stooped and Mamie had long since departed to a far-off city, this ceremony persisted. While he marked the trunks we would say, "Do you remember how you used to wave to Mamie Brady?" and he would nod and chuckle. It was our first unforgettable glimpse of village romance.

But in the sea captain's days there were, of course, no railroad tracks—only a few neighbors; and the bridge over the river was wooden and not the black iron one that was familiar to us. No doubt the captain had hoped to find in this peaceful place a haven in his old age when his voyaging was done. But he and his son were both lost at sea only four years after he built the house. Of his widow and the rest of his family little was recorded, though it was known that at one time his fourteen-year-old daughter had been arrested for the very quaint crime of walking out on Sunday with a young man. There was, too, that cruel tale of a Negro who had been walled up alive in the cellar, and whose ghost was supposed to haunt the house. If this was true, his spirit walked without malevolence and silently, for I do not remember that he was ever seen or heard in our time. Or perhaps, as the years went on, the house gathered unto itself so many other ghosts that he found company enough on his own plane, and so left the living undisturbed.

Certainly the house was well situated to receive guests from the dead as well as from the quick, for the garden behind it and to the side was separated only by a walled embankment from an old burying-ground. Here lay most of the original settlers of the town and their descendants, some under slabs of lichened granite or peeling sandstone, some beneath tombs of marble once white and made like tables, with lengthy dissertations and quotations cut into the flat tops. On the vertical headstones the names and dates were finished off with some severe little verse or the carving of a winged head. These bodiless angels all wore the same expression of grim contempt, no doubt from looking down on earth and its sinful ways.

Sometimes people would remark that they thought it must be disquieting to live as close as we did to so many graves, but my grandfather always replied, "They are the best neighbors I have ever had."

All the children in the neighborhood, ourselves included, considered the old cemetery their special, private, and beloved playground. Wild flowers grew there, mingled with the creeping myrtle planted by mourners long ago, and on the grassy hillside by a tumbled wall the smallest and the sweetest wild strawberries ripened in the sun. Beyond the burying-ground there were fields, an orchard, and two narrow brooks that broke over small pebbles, bubbling into silver with a low, monotonous, and entrancing sound, and harboring an occasional iridescent trout. Death lost its sting somewhat in a place so secret, and so deserted except for the orioles flashing in and out of the weeping willows and the voices of children as they climbed into the gnarled apple trees to reach for the red fruit in the fall or, late in the spring, to shake down a drift of pink-and-white petals over the long-forgotten graves.

There were only three acres around our house, but little by little my grandfather had planted it with trees—five maples across the front, a linden with arching branches on the bank where the front lawn sloped up into the broader space on the side, and pines and hemlocks along each borderline between his land and the neighbors'. There was ample room for a vegetable garden and flower beds and, behind the house close to the back wall, a red barn with a long covered shed set at right angles to it. Wherever he could, he put in fruit trees, a Seckel pear or a black cherry, a russet apple tree and several red astrachans.

At some time in his life he seemed to have amused himself experimenting in a small way with grafting, for there was one tree that for a while bore two varieties of fruit, one on each side. This tree always puzzled me and I would often stand and stare at it. For eating, the russet apples with their harsh, dark-golden skins were the juiciest, but the red astrachans were silkier to hold in the hand and their flesh was white and delicately flavored. They were an early apple, and as I lay awake on warm nights I would be startled to hear one dully strike the ground or fall on the roof of the latticed summerhouse, bouncing off into the grass.

Between the garden and the lawn stretched a long arbor covered with a grapevine. There early in the fall hung the heavy purple clusters, filling the air with fragrance. On the other side of the arbor grew the gooseberry bushes and the red and white currants, the tiny globes of fruit translucent and streaked with minute veins, suspended under dainty green leaves. In summer a hedge of sweet peas crossed the wide end of the garden, tilting their colored blossoms into the sunshine like an endless procession of fairy sunbonnets. Red tomatoes warm from the vine, or peas scooped out of their shells into a grubby little palm, tasted a hundred times sweeter than they did when they came, steaming and seasoned, to the supper table. And the rows of corn, with their bladelike leaves that could cut a cheek or a wrist so stingingly and their blond strands of silk, the browned ends falling over onto the swollen ears, seemed like an endless tropical forest whose stately tassels brushed against the blue sky itself.

Our closest neighbor was elderly Miss Bateman in the house next above ours on the River Road. But as the pine trees between our places were thick and dark, and as she lived almost the life of a recluse, alone except for a sedate maidservant her own age, we were seldom aware of the personality behind her neatly curtained windows. Occasionally she sent roses to us from her small garden, and often on Sunday noons when the dessert happened to be especially worthy of our household, Ned and I were delegated to carry some of it over to Miss Bateman. Ned went along to ring the bell, so that I could use both hands on the dish of dessert, but we both went willingly enough, because we liked Miss Bateman.

Miss Bateman wore an impressive iron-gray wig, which we always considered a worth-while sight no matter how often we saw it. She would come to the door herself for the dessert, a short, stout woman something like Queen Victoria in her dress, and perhaps in her manner too. In addition to the wig, Miss Bateman had another and even greater distinction—that of being a divorced woman, undoubtedly the only one of her period in Norwich Town. She further astonished the community by remaining on good terms with her husband, and Sunday afternoons in summer he often came there to call. Sitting side by side in squeaky rockers on her vined front porch, they would chat rather formally in low tones. He was a small, meek-looking man in carefully brushed black clothes whose identity had been completely submerged in divorce—as a woman's is in marriage—for he was never referred to by anyone except as "Miss Bateman's husband."

The house on the other side was much older than Miss Bateman's, and though once dignified and well-cared-for, it had deteriorated into the shabby shelter for three families. Fortunately it was not close to us, and on this side too there was a screen of trees, but it was still near enough for us to hear the Clancy family in their liveliest moments. Sad-faced Mrs. Bingham lived there too, with her lame son and her pretty, questionable daughter, whom she supported by taking in washing and working out by the day. The top floor was occupied by old Mr. Donahue, a respectable workingman, and his wizened, neat wife.

Pat Clancy, also a workingman but not at all respectable, and his family had the rest of the house. Both parents were the big, rawboned, red-faced type of Irish, and as Kate's right arm was as strong as Clancy's any day, he knew exactly what to expect—and no doubt what to hope for—on those Saturday nights when he returned home well liquored, and in just the right mood for a fracas. Occasionally, judging by the sounds, it seemed as though some of the younger Clancys joined in the cries of battle, if not in the battle itself.

Yet out of this tangle of wild Irish had sprung one rose —a daughter, Katie, just about my own age. She and I often met at the wall under the pine trees between our two yards. We would play quietly there on the floor of brown needles, or go questing farther on into the garden or the old burying-ground. Kate Clancy had some special pride in this fragile little girl, for she kept her hair in shining order and her worn dresses were always clean. Katie never had much to say, waiting timidly for my suggestions, but there was something eagerly responsive in the way she followed whatever path I chose to take, smiling her wistful smile and running ever so lightly on bare brown feet.

I always think of the outside of our house as surrounded by summer; inside, it seems to be, at least for those earliest years, more often some scene in winter. We may be at the breakfast table, my grandfather, my mother, my father, my two brothers, and myself. The white sunlight flashes in through the pointed spears of icicles hanging outside the windows. It picks out dazzling sparks in the silver and glazes the surface of the immaculate white tablecloth. Hannah comes in from the kitchen bearing the coffeepot, its spout sending forth a little cloud of aromatic steam. We children have our fresh milk, which Fred, "the man," has brought down that morning from his own small farm a mile or two away. It is richly white, its tiny bright bubbles clustering around the edges of our silver cups. My cup is shaped like a sturdy urn and has my name written on its side inside a raised wreath of leaves and flowers. "A prettier shape for a girl," they had said when they bought it, attracted by its contrast with the boys' plainer mugs.

Just across the doorsill lies Leo, the Irish setter, his brown eyes fixed upon this gathering from which he accepts his exclusion, but always a little sadly. As we chatter in our curious human fashion, his long-fringed tail beats softly on the floor, but only occasionally and with courteous restraint.

Our breakfast was always immense and merciless. We would have sliced oranges, big bowls of cereal, platters of corn bread cut into squares, or hot biscuits or muffins, or "fried bread," or—at the least and dullest—towering plates of crisp toast. There would be bacon or sausages and eggs, or mackerel (fishballs always on Sunday morning), or tripe, or even lamb chops and creamed potatoes. I was the only one who balked at this laden table. Just about half-way through my oatmeal the whole idea of breakfast would pall, and much parental urging would then begin. Finally my grandfather, from the head of the table that then seemed so far distant to me, would lean forward and say:

"What, child, no porridge? Why, it'll warm your little gizzard." And after a moment of scrutinizing me in his amused way he would add, "That young one don't eat enough to physic a snipe."

Then he would give me a prodigious wink that screwed up the whole side of his face. Much abashed, I would plunge my spoon into the apparently bottomless bowl.

The meal over at last, the day, now we were so heavily fortified, can begin. My mother goes out to the kitchen to confer with Hannah. Far away, on the other side of the house, I hear the faint jingle of sleigh bells—Fred hitching up Charlie to take my father and my grandfather into the town and my brother Sam to school. The family horse, during a succession of beasts, always bore the name Charlie, amplified in leisurely moments into Charles Augustus.

Now my father is helping my grandfather into his coat —that dignified, rather formal affair of broadcloth with a cape. He wears a wide-brimmed hat with a low, round crown—a "shovel hat"—and he comes slowly down the hall, his cane hung over his arm. He is a small old man with silvery-white hair and a white mustache and beard clipped close to his ruddy face. Once he moved briskly and with abundant vitality, but now his step is reluctantly restrained. Only the blue eyes in their network of quizzical lines are still keen and darting.

Behind him comes my father's tall, erect figure, the dark head held high. His face, with its heavy eyebrows and the long mustache of the nineties, is gentle and a little melancholy. "Now, Mr. Hoyt . . ." he says to his father-in-law in his quiet voice. He opens the door for the old man and helps him down the steps to the path, their feet crunching in the dry, dazzling snow. Impatient Sam has already gone out and is in the sleigh at the gate. Both Fred and Charlie are blowing out clouds of steam into the sparkling air, and Fred has small icicles on his sandy, tobacco-stained mustache. He is wrapped in a muffler and keeps flinging one red-mittened hand against the opposite shoulder to warm himself.

Inside, at the window my mother, Ned, and I are standing to watch this splendid, this important daily departure. The two men tuck themselves into the blankets on the back seat of the sleigh, with Sam between them. The sleigh slowly glides off down the white road under the black arches of the leafless maple trees. Charlie's pace grows brisker, and through the frosted window pane I hear that sweetest and most shivery of all delicate sounds, the jubilant peal of sleigh bells, shattering the perfect stillness of an old-fashioned winter morning.

CHAPTER VI

THE ATTIC

POSSIBLY only a dreamy child can fully grasp—or wants to—the difference between a family storeroom, an attic, and the public secondhand shop, and perhaps the difference is important only to herself. But all old junk, even when it has belonged to strangers, must vibrate in the imagination of sensitive observers with many exquisite overtones. If the junk consists of objects once loved, used, worn, or made by those of one's own blood, they assume an inescapable and tender significance. Even when the object is ludicrous, one's laughter is gentle.

A child wandering among such outcast but still surviving fragments of other times, other lives, sees herself not as an isolated figure, shelterless and undirected, but as a partaker, a marcher in a long processional that has passed under this, her very own roof. Death is diminished for her, and life enlarged. For better or for worse, the incidents of her own hearth reach out and merge in the events of her country's history. She comes to have both a respect and a disregard for Time that are somewhat Chinese. She knows that the past and the future are closely integrated, yet as distinctly separate as the two sides of a medal, and that her appreciation of the present is measured by the strength of her desire to hold that medal in the hollow of her hand, to scrutinize it, to remember, and to dream.

And so the attic in my grandfather's house became more than just another room in the house. It was the very breath and body of the whole eventful rooftree. Like a family memory-book, it contained a keepsake for everybody, from someone's old doll to someone else's rusty sword. There was a bride's bouquet crumbling to dust in a box, and near by, where it had been set on a shelf neatly tied up in a package, was the groom's hat, the crushable kind, and I was endlessly amused pushing it open and smashing it shut.

Backed up against the chimney, accumulating a rich patina of neglect, stood a maple highboy that in the later years of appreciation was borne forth with tenderness and amid a babble of voices. But to me at that time it was no more exciting than several other objects, one afterward identified as a pewter bedpan, or than the round tin tub with flaring sides, or the walking-machine in which a baby had stood, supported on a little wheeled device, to experiment with his first feeble steps. One of the more violent children, it seemed, had walked in it across the porch, straight down the steps and away.

One large square trunk held some of the pretty belongings of a belle of the 1870's—pale pink and blue brocades with bustles and pearl trimmings on the bodices, thin silver bangles, rosebud earrings of coral, a feather fan with pearl sticks, and a small black-lace parasol, the ivory handle delicately carved. To complete this gay chapter in her life, as I afterwards learned it downstairs, there should have been one other item that was missing—a pair of slippers with the heels stripped off.

She had had a devoted but jealous beau, evidently a serious fellow who not only writhed at the sight of her dancing with other men but disapproved altogether of the idea of dancing. So, after what must have been rather a high-pitched scene, he stole a pair of her slippers, tore off the heels, and left them in a reproachful little heap outside her door. I used to wonder where the heels were. Had she thrown them away, chagrined? Or did she indignantly bear them off to the shoemaker's to be put back on and to end their days in the polka?

Another trunk held the children's clothes, the hemstitched lawn bonnets, the woolen petticoats with scalloped edges, and the long embroidered christening robes of infancy. Some of these things had their stories too, like that one of the little boy just old enough in the year 1849 to say plaintively, "I want a new pair of boots, a pair that *squeaks!*" And there they were to prove the story. And some years after this, a little girl playing around the front gate was hailed by a passing neighbor.

"My, Mary, how nice you look!"

"You think so?" said Mary in some surprise. "Well, you ought to see me Sundays!"

Some of Mary's pantalettes and a pair of her small lace mitts lay folded away together. Perhaps she wore those very ones on that theatrical day in the meetinghouse when, driven by pity knows what childish interpretation of the revivalist's roaring, she fled up the aisle with streaming eyes to take her place on the sinners' bench. Beside her, somewhat astonished at this addition to their group, sat the usual "fallen woman" and the "town drunkard."

About the year 1890, a little boy had a suit with a jacket trimmed with brass buttons, and kilts, which were worn over a pair of trousers to match. The boys at school made fun of his kilts and called them skirts, but his mother admired them very much. On his way to school there was a tunnel where the brook ran under the road. There he used to leave the kilts, proceeding on his way in his trousers, and on his return dressing himself again in the kilts and so home to his mother. The whole suit, looking hardly worn at all—particularly the kilts—had been cherished and put away in the attic.

How many times they must have said, "What shall we do with this?" after the ball, the wedding, the christening, the funeral—and the answer appears to have been always the same—"Ah, well, put it away in the attic." It became almost a family refrain. It seems as if such a weight of Time must have pressed the old house farther and farther down into the earth on which it stood. And the books, and the letters—it is almost impossible to describe the quantity or the curiosity or the pathos of those. As to the letters, the intimate quality of their contents can be imagined from a remark of my grandfather's, which was often repeated in my hearing as a little girl.

During the course of his long and busy life he had accumulated a store of anecdotes and legends about Connecticut, but mostly about the families in the town of Norwich, where his family began, from which they had wandered only to return, and where, between intervals of political activity which drew him from home, he had lived for so many years. One evening when he had been amusing a group of friends with some of these tales, one lady was moved by her appreciation to remark:

"Let's hire Breed Hall and get Judge Hoyt to stand up and tell all he knows about Norwich."

My grandfather turned to her with a chuckle and said:

"If I should ever stand up in Breed Hall and tell *all* I know about Norwich, Connecticut, I would be like St. Stephen of old—stoned to death!"

But among all that accumulation of stale scandal and notes on startling or just commonplace human dramas, there lay scattered much that had interest of a more innocent and nonetheless appealing variety.

A girl in the 1870's who went to a seminary in New Haven had kept several epistles written to her by her schoolmates shortly before her marriage. By that time they had all been out of school for several years but, judging by their words, they still kept a strict faith in the high value of spinsterhood. Some of them reproached her so passionately for her decision to become a wedded woman that she must have shuddered at the implications in their phrases. At that period, it seems, matrimony was not a beginning or even an end. It was The End. And among these tearful salutations of farewell lay a faded photograph that showed all the young ladies of the seminary playing croquet on the lawn in hats and gloves.

Under the eaves, amid a heap of packing-cases, there was a small haircloth trunk, its rounded top studded with brass nails. It contained packets of letters, neatly arranged according to date, from the nineteen-year-old boy who had died in the Battle of Antietam. With the letters, according to the morbid sentiment of the time, was the bullet that gave him the fatal one of his several wounds. On the cover of the box containing it his mother had written in her delicate Victorian hand "The Minnie Ball that killed my son."

That soldier's letters had a strange and very strong fascination for me. They laid on my heart so keen a personal emotion about the Civil War that it seemed like no other war ever waged on earth. I read them so often and with such unmistakable signs of suffering that it became a family joke. "Where's Sister?" one brother would ask, and the other would reply, "Aw, she's up in the attic bawling over the Civil War."

They never saw that soldier as I did. They had their own heroes in the family past, like Philemon Hale, the privateer who gave his crew a mixture of rum and gunpowder before attacking a British ship, or Jonathan Adgate, a surgeon in the Revolutionary Army. So the Civil War soldier, his letters and his memory, became my own. And how often certain phrases he had written would spring up in my mind as I listened to the conversations of older people, and sometimes, vividly, in the history class at school. He had seen the dead on the battlefields, "and they all had terrible wounds." Or the other boys, after battles, were taking trophies, but "my conscience wouldn't let me." And in putting off his mother's evidently often-repeated plea to have his picture taken, he replied sheepishly, using an odd bit of old-fashioned slang:

"Perhaps I'll be a captain. Then, you know, I shall have a forky old pair of shoulder straps, and the picture will look gay."

Most memorable of all was that grim little vignette of a fallen enemy.

> In the fort, just behind the embrasure, was the body of a Rebel lieutenant. He was young and very handsome. He had on nice fine underclothes and they were as neat as wax. They were marked "W. D. Selden, Richmond Blues." His pockets were turned inside out, his gold watch gone, part of the chain alone remaining, and some vandal had carried the joke so far as to cut off his goatee.

Looking down on that other dead boy, did the writer have the slightest foreboding that he saw himself, his own stripped body, like a reflection in a blood-stained mirror?

"You must stop worrying about me, my dear mother," he wrote. "There is not the slightest danger of my being killed."

And so all that, too, was "put away in the attic."

Nobody in the household paid much attention to my solitary rummaging in the attic, except the time that I discovered a small packet of Dr. Jonathan Adgate's letters.

They had fallen down behind a row of books and lain there long forgotten. Most of them were copies of his own sent to others, his handwriting still quite clear and legible. Those he had received look very unusual to me because they had no stamps and no envelope. They were simply folded over, broken seals still on the flaps. This discovery, when carried downstairs for explanation, precipitated one more of those moments of noble resolution when my mother and my father agreed they *must* "go through" the attic.

I was excited myself to know that I had happened on the same Dr. Adgate whose powderhorn lay on the library mantelpiece. I had often studied its inscription—"Doct. Jonathan Adgate, His Horn, Fort Edward, Sept. 29, 1758" —and the engraved pictures of a surgical saw, an amputating knife, a griffinlike kind of figure, and the British coat of arms. Sometimes, too, I had tried to decipher the sentences in a small notebook he had carried, his "selected Medical Elaborata," in which he had set down remedies for everything from "moist, running ulcers," to "soporific heaviness."

Not only the long strange words astonished me, but also the names of medicines, some of which I knew as flowers, such as artemisia, mugwort, arum, and wake-robin. Of the first he had written, "an infusion is sometimes drank as an anti-hysteric, used among the females," and of the second, "the root fresh is a powerful stimulant in cachetic and chlorotic habits." The notebook was dated 1802, and since by then he had lived through two wars and witnessed much human agony, its very first notation was most significant of all—"Opium, the hand of God, one of our greatest blessings."

He must have had skillful hands to accomplish what he did with no help but the most primitive of instruments. They did not work unrecognized, however, for his commanding officer wrote: "Dr. Adgate is blessed with a natural insight into Wounds and Dexterity in treating them peculiar to himself." And at least one curious affliction that he relieved was described in an item in the *Norwich Packet* for April 1777:

> Dr. Adgate has recently extracted the bone of an alewife from the throat of Mr. Ebenezer Lord, where it had been lodged for twenty-five years, and at various times had given him exquisite pain. It was about the size of a brown thread needle, and was barbed from end to end.

The books in the attic had been stacked or piled or shoved in anywhere with no attempt at arrangement. Over on the shelves by the door was an assortment including everyone's primers and grammars, English, Latin, French, and Greek. There were Bibles, of course, ranging in size from one no bigger than your thumb to one so large and bulky that I carried it in my arms when I took it across to the window to read. On the flyleaf of that one, in bold, black handwriting, was a man's name, the year 1629, and the words "Essex, England." The other big books, bound in worn leather, were an Apocrypha with engravings and several volumes of the laws of early Connecticut with very stately lettering. There were sermons and treatises and Sunday-school books. There was a grimly illustrated *Medical History of the Civil War,* in which I could see for myself, if I had doubted it, that "they all had terrible wounds." Two volumes contained startling pictures, and accounts of heroic ladies who went along with their husbands in the Union Army. Their hair hung loosely and untidily on their shoulders, like Indians' locks, whether they were in dashing riding-costume with a seven-shooter at the belt or wore trousers like the men, surmounted by a modest knee-length tunic, and carried a sergeant's straight sword.

Evidently someone in the family, or perhaps more than one, had been interested in all kinds of extraordinary women for a long time. A shabby old book called *A Vindication of the Rights of Women* lay at the bottom of a heap, but it had no pictures, and its long, antique *s*'s made it difficult reading. A fat volume labeled *Eminent Women of the Age* in gold letters was less puzzling. And there were portraits of them all too, everyone from Queen Victoria to Rosa Bonheur, from Julia Ward Howe and Margaret Fuller Ossoli to Mrs. Sigourney. Mrs. Sigourney had lived in Norwich, and I often came on her poems in anthologies or in scrapbooks full of stained clippings.

There was plenty of poetry, both English and American—stout collected works of Tennyson, Byron, and Longfellow, illustrated editions of Whittier and Poe and others. A thin book called *M'Fingal* enchanted me with its humorous pictures. I also dug out of its contents the incredible tale of the British soldiers walking on Beacon Hill at sunset who ran away from June bugs terrified, thinking that they were bullets.

This story, like that one told me by my father of the redcoats who fled in the night from Windham because the bullfrogs sounded like an approaching army, convinced me that the English must be an easily scared nation. But I felt sure that the frogs of Windham had been a mighty race, for the strength of their song was the subject of several legends. These, and many more about all the towns of Connecticut, I found in one book with both covers and some of the pages gone. Somehow such curious trivia lodged in the corners of my mind, like inescapable, queer-shaped pieces of some big picture puzzle that I was trying to reassemble.

I learned that Norwich was once called "The Rose of New England," and that she was famous for the size of her puddings, while New London was noted for that of her dumplings. I often sat wondering what it would have meant to be a guest at tripe suppers, turtle entertainments, or the ordination parties where the clergy displayed such enthusiasm and skill in making punch. But these meditative moments were the mild ones. I read faster when I came to stories of wolves in the swamps around New London, or of the huge black snakes in the Norwich Town meadows, or of the Indians who were everywhere.

Those two chiefs, shrewd Uncas and that other with his rippling, melodic name, Miantonomo, I never forgot. They hated and feared and admired each other for a long time, but it was Uncas who, with the help of the English, finally won out. Proud of his victory, he was no less proud of his enemy, for as he stood over the body of the slain Miantonomo, he drew out his long knife and, slicing off pieces of the still warm flesh, he ate them and said:

"It is good. It is sweet. It will make my heart strong."

It was somewhat disappointing to find that only one

witch had been hanged in Connecticut. But she haunted me because she was only a girl, and her name, Alse, suggested nothing evil. And altogether, she, the wolves, the snakes, and the Indian chiefs seemed as mythical to read about as some of the records left as to the behavior of nature itself in the various townships—as, for instance, the mountain in Moodus that "made noises," or "the rock that walked" on the shore near New London, or the island in the Connecticut River that quietly vanished away.

As a contrast to all this wild, dark, mysterious poetry, there were later substantial figures like Sarah Knight, a very lively lady who finally settled down at Norwich. Early in the eighteenth century she journeyed through New England, keeping a journal as she went. Apparently equally afraid of a "hors" or a "cannoo," she nevertheless managed to traverse much earth and water. Among many observant comments on people and towns, she mentioned divorces—"stand aways," she called them—and considered them entirely "too much in vougue" among both the English and the Indians.

Sometimes, in trying moments, she found it restful to set down her thoughts in verse. Her phrase for this was "Composing my Resentments," and she resorted to it late one night in a Connecticut tavern when some quarrelsome topers in the room next to hers kept her too long awake. She lit her candle in despair and wrote:

> I ask thy aid, O potent Rum,
> To charm these wrangling Topers dum.
> Thou hast their giddy brains possesst,
> The man confounded with the Beast—
> And I, poor I, can get no rest.

Intoxicate them with thy fumes,
O still their Tongues till morning comes!

The charm worked, for she added that "the dispute soon ended with t'other dram."

Naturally the attic had no scholarly feeling for the sequence of events. On those shelves and in those boxes and trunks, the decades and the centuries all gathered dust impartially together. I, the contented living child, ran my exploring hand along the rows of books, pulling one out here or there, gathering in my variegated store richly and carelessly, much as a magpie picks up sparkling bits of stone, ribbon, or refuse and carries them all home to its nest. If I was interested one minute to think of Lady Fenwick and her crumbling grave on the shore at Saybrook, I was equally so the next to imagine the Duc de Lauzun, that elegant French nobleman, sulking in the village of Lebanon and longing for the gaiety of Newport. That a hundred years and more, brimful of other lives and events, stretched between this lady and this gentleman would not have disconcerted me very much, even had I happened to count them.

In the attic history shrank, but the lives, as I came upon them, seemed distinct and important, each in its own niche. And the place was so cluttered that it took my mind no longer to dart across the decades, and even from war to war, than it took my eyes to glance from the Union soldier's sword across to the cedar-lined medicine chest that had belonged to the Revolutionary doctor. Perhaps the fact that some of my own discarded toys had found their resting-place up here may have assured me that all the other objects in some way belonged to me as well. My own old doll house with one door off, standing as it did beside a broken spinning wheel, perhaps gave me the impression that one was really no more unfamiliar than the other. They were simply companions in disuse. I never seemed to question why either had been saved. I accepted them, as indeed I accepted the whole attic, as a necessary and comprehensible part of the more orderly rooms downstairs—and so too a part of me myself.

PART II

CHAPTER VII

DR. JONATHAN ADGATE, APPRENTICE TO AESCULAPIUS

1740-1815

DR. JONATHAN ADGATE'S life began mildly enough in Norwich Town in 1740. It ended in New York City in 1815 in a rage. The seventy-five years between those two dates were eventful enough to have satisfied several men, even had they all been as energetic, courageous, and determined as Jonathan himself.

That anger of his, which consumed the last fifteen years of his existence, had its beginning—or some of it—in his sudden impulse at the age of sixty to leave Norwich for New York. Norwich, always reluctant to blame itself for any resentment on the part of its citizens, decided that the reason for Dr. Adgate's violent uprooting was merely the preference for a city practice. The town rather smugly explained that both his age and his reputation now demanded a field that was broader and easier as well as more lucrative. In 1801 he himself, in a letter to no less a personage than President Jefferson, gave quite another reason:

> I have left my native home, domestic happiness, and an extensive practice of Physic and Surgery to get away from the bitter, envious and mischievous Clergy of Connecticut, who I have been publickly abused by, all on acco't of Electioneering. I have resided in New York for twelve months past, where I wish to continue and move my family.

His grievance against the church could not have been all-inclusive, for he copied out a reverent and passionate appeal to Jefferson, either written by a Connecticut minister or delivered by him from the pulpit, and sent it to the President:

> Thos. Jefferson, president of the United States—Beloved patriot, among the unaccountable bustles of time, don't give out—the day's your own, your philosophic defence is equal to the task, we are never more unhappy than when we think or hear of your leaving government, the control of our national affairs; we have nowhere else to go but unto thee, in time of trouble, pray suffer us once more to elect you Head of the nation, wherein you preside, four years in addition to your elected period will bring us into that blessed Aera, when the nations of the

earth will be at peace, and the presiding chiefs in glory, you if not the first, never to be eclipsed, conscious of thine own happiness to eternity.

Jonathan's irritation at the church's interference in his affairs represented only a small part of his general discontent. His real enemy, he felt, was his country, which had neglected to pay him as fully as he thought he deserved for so many years of service in the army. He did not know Jefferson, nor Madison, to whom he wrote on a later occasion, nor many of the others who received his bitter and plaintive appeals. Nevertheless, these were sent continuously and rapidly to Secretaries of War and Treasury, to military leaders and Congressmen, and also to friends, now holding important positions, whom he had known during the course of the Revolution.

His frenzy had at least one compensation. It induced him to set down some part of his long record, which otherwise he would never have had the vanity or the patience to do. Whatever impression, if any, his disjointed and ungrammatical sentences made on Thomas Jefferson, they were read by one of his children with a melancholy devotion. His daughter Felicity, then a spinster in her thirties, sometimes copied his letters for him. There, for the first time, she could see plainly emerging from his urgent words the figure of this man as he had been in her childhood. There lay the explanation of that shadowy—almost mythical—father who had never been at home for long under his own roof, but who had come and gone, a weary guest in the shabby uniform of a soldier. She found much of the whole story in this one letter:

I served them as a satisfactory officer from the beginning of our late war with Great Britain to the end, attending their sick and wounded brewing my hands with corruption and blood, at the first action of Bunker-Hill, the wounded of the Squadron of commodore Hopkins in the action with a British frigate in block Island sound, bro't into New London and attended there, at New York in our retreat from thence, Harlem, White plains, up and down the north river, at the storm of fort Montgomery, the burning of Danbury, fairfield, Norwalk, New London, Groton, and monmouth New Jersey, all these places I were at, and everywhere else my assistance was solicited and courted, always ready to serve them, at all seasons of the year, marching for 30, or 40, miles of a cold winters night to attack fort independence, suffering for a number of days beyond measure, with cold and hunger; all these things I went through, the fatigue of the war, unpaid, barr'd by the act of limitation.

With great firmness he expressed his feeling of special pride in his own branch of the service, and his strong conviction of its value throughout the course of the Revolution, or "this grand dispute," as he sometimes called the war.

. . . many of us had been in service since ye war began . . . attending ye wounded [and] Pestilential, Putrid, Malignant and Contagious cases in confined hospitals. More dangerous our lives, more exposed than they would have been in any Action of ye Field . . . [while] perhaps many of ye Officers of ye Line . . . have not seen a kernal of powder burnt while in Service.

Often before plunging into his own concerns and demands he began his letters to a President on an ingratiating note of sympathy. He wrote to Madison in June 1814:

There is no one feels more for the present administration and government than I do. Your . . . faithfulness is equal to support you under all abuse. There is a dam'd crew in the world and we can't help it. They must be suffered to go to Hell their own way. Here you find I have grown mad.

And mad he was, though not demented. Now, too, some of his vexation, instigated by the jealousy of an aging man who felt himself set aside, was directed against the young in his profession:

> Some of them do not know the use of a common lancet, nor the dressing of a simple wound. . . . It cannot be supposed that young men, who never saw a gunshot wound, should know how to manage them, all gunshot wounds in their nature, ever so simple, are always more or less dangerous, and on those attended with sphacelations from lacerated flesh, fractured bones, &c. &c. the greatest medical skill is required. . . . I fear our wounded all around us are Suffering from the want of the aid of those who are practically informed.

He wrote that in 1813, when he was experiencing his third war as an army surgeon. He could not believe that he was old or set in his ways. He doubted the young men and their novelties and innovations. He forgot the honorable efforts of his own youth against ignorance and conservatism, his battles against quackery, his losing struggle, years before the Revolution, to introduce such a dangerous idea as smallpox inoculation. And of medical colleges, now starting in America, he was skeptical, believing, as he said:

> A Man ought to be born for the Science of physic and surgery, and know well the use of his Head and hands. It is not all the researches and inquiries of Chymistry under the Heaven that would make a physician or surgeon.

Yet he did not by any means despise books. The year after the Revolution ended, when he delivered a series of lectures in Connecticut, his "prospectus" addressed to "the rising sons of Aesculapius" not only offered them lessons in "Anatomy, Physic, Surgery, etc." together with the "advantage of being present at capital operations, dissections, etc.," but also promised them free access to "a complete library of ancient and modern authors." His own interest in medical writings continued to the end. Even in 1810, while he was so constantly and industriously showering those personal pleas in every direction, he found time for this letter to Richard Reece in London:

Dear Sir, There is no one better pleased with your medical arrangements than I am, especially your medical guide, and dictionary think it a great pity they were not published on better paper, the family medicine chest, termed the family dispensary complete, Caton on venereal disease and Cow pox, Hooper's Anatomist vade mecum; with compendious medical dictionary the latest and best edition, his diagram of the Eye with explanations, and his thoracic and abdominal viscera all colored Denmans Vectis, and Lithotomia cachee, both neatly finished. Please to send the above articles pr. the Bearer Capt. Eldridge and the Bill, that it may be acknowledged and paid agreeable to your expectation, on his return to London, or the first opportunity, let them all be of the first quality and the Books in Boards—

At fifteen, after the death of his own father, Jonathan Adgate was adopted by Dr. Eliphalet Leffingwell, a man of benevolent nature and prosperous family connections, who had been practicing in Norwich since his graduation from Yale in 1738. In the Leffingwell household Jonathan became not only a foster son but a disciple. There were then no medical schools in the country, and though he and the Doctor undoubtedly knew that students from New York and Philadelphia, as well as from cities all over the world, were assembling in Edinburgh to work under the most brilliant and original teachers of the eighteenth century, they did not consider such a course for Jonathan. He merely did what other medical apprentices did with other older physicians in Connecticut. He "rode" with Dr. Leffingwell. This privilege of "riding" meant accompanying the Doctor on his rounds in order to study his methods and his patients, and at home helping to compound his medicines and keep his books.

Dr. Leffingwell had no son of his own, but there were three daughters, Lucy, Nancy and Deborah, all younger than Jonathan. They thought it great fun to have a brother, though they were often subdued by the air of importance that he always assumed in their presence. Clip-clopping on their pattens over the dewy stones that led down to the garden, they would peek in at him through the window of the Doctor's office, a small room under the slanting roof at the rear of the house. Jonathan would be standing at work there in his stained homespun smock, bent over the pine table, his hands busy with the small stone mortar and pestle. Behind him and around him were shelves full of earthen jars and odd-shaped bottles gleaming with pale liquids. With his black locks falling across his forehead, his large light-gray eyes very serious, he looked not unlike a sorcerer's boy concocting magic potions. If one of the little girls ever ventured into that room to beg Jonathan for a look at the leeches swimming in their big crock, she never stayed long, for he was inclined to sprinkle some evil-smelling powder down her neck or in her hair.

In one corner of the garden Dr. Leffingwell grew many

of his own medicinal plants. Lucy, like a good daughter, knew and named them all many times to Jonathan—the sweet-scented thyme that subdued fevers, the bitter boneset, helpful for colds, the hoarhound, a cure for consumption, the spikenard and the lovage, the tansy, the spearmint and the balm. And always, coming to the sage, she would rub one of the rough leaves between her finger and thumb, repeating the Latin words that her father had taught her—"*Cur moriatur homo, dum salis crescit in horto?*"

Most of all Lucy and her sisters liked to go with Jonathan across the town to Dr. Lathrop's drugstore, where he went occasionally on errands. This establishment had won considerable fame for itself, as it was the only place of its kind between New York and Boston. Dr. Lathrop, the owner, had decided early in his career that he was too tenderhearted for surgery, and so had concentrated on the apothecary's trade, spending three years in England learning this branch of his profession. He imported quantities of drugs, and supervised their sale and distribution with the utmost care. One of the apprentices in this shop, a boy about Jonathan's age named Ben Arnold, had a lurid fascination for the Leffingwell girls. He was cruel to birds, he loved thunderstorms, and once he had run away because he wanted to join the British Army. Standing close to Jonathan, their solemn faces shadowed by the folds of their soft camlet hoods, they would stare at this lamentable hero while he measured out Jonathan's order on the brass scales.

Jonathan himself thought a good deal about soldiering during these years when Connecticut was sending hundreds of men into the North to fight for their king against the French and the Indians. Finally in 1758, when he was eighteen, he enlisted in a company from Norwich Town, first as a private, although the following year he received a commission as surgeon's assistant.

Dr. Leffingwell was proud of this action of his foster son's, though for his own part he would never have chosen the army for the practice of surgery. He enjoyed the dignity and the comfort of his position in his own community, and he did everything to maintain and enhance it. His yellow house, one of the first to be painted in Norwich Town, had wainscoted rooms and a staircase noticeable for the delicacy of its balustrade, which turned at a landing. In his corner cupboard, amid flowered china, stood the largest and the most decorative toddy glass in town, and one of his hearths boasted a Franklin stove. His two admirable African slaves, Fortune and his wife Time, lived in their own quarters at the rear of the house.

The Doctor bought his daughters fawn-colored silks and embroidered muslins, and his wife even owned muffs and a beaver hat. His own clothes were of excellent broadcloth, and his periwig, which curled upward from an already high forehead, inspired awe in his patients. Perhaps even more they reverenced his orange-colored cloak and his cane, in the head of which was inserted a silver pomander containing the powder of some aromatic disinfectant. When he tapped the cane, the sickroom became momentarily refreshingly fragrant. He made a point of tapping twice when he entered and twice as he departed, a ritual of hail and farewell peculiar to himself.

Such cheerful pomposity was alien to Jonathan's nature

and even slightly repugnant to him. He went about the business of healing in a forthright way of his own. In fact Dr. Leffingwell considered his deportment almost disconcertingly plain and blunt. Perhaps if the older man could have followed Jonathan into the Canadian wilderness, he would have admitted that there so ornate a professional style as his own would be as much out of place as his grogram waistcoats. It might impress—and often did—lying-in females or dropsical gentlemen, cozily ailing within their curtained beds. But it could hardly be affected by a physician whose hands, blue with cold, strove to minister not too brutally to mutilated men, either lying where they had fallen or, at best, brought up to a tent or a log hut on a dog sledge that left behind it a zigzag trail of blood freezing on the snow.

Jonathan did not return to Norwich and the Leffingwells for five years, but this long exile was his schooling. There were no holidays, no frolics or festivities, and the rewards were only of the austere kind bestowed upon a young man who delighted in hardship and self-reliance. He was not too proud to learn what he could from the Indians nor too modest to seek instruction from the British surgeons. Some of the Englishmen took a fancy to the serious, well-mannered young American and invited him to witness their capital operations. Unless liquor happened to be at hand, or their patient thoughtfully fainted, they had no way of dulling the horror and the pain. They could rely only on their resourcefulness and skill, and often their performances seemed to Jonathan like sleight-of-hand, their fingers moved so cleverly and so fast.

When the war ended early in 1763, Jonathan thought almost reluctantly of returning home; he was at heart as much of a soldier as a surgeon. He had grown accustomed to danger and excitement, and he found it difficult to imagine himself settling down into the routine of a second Dr. Leffingwell, patiently attending to such quiet, minor ailments as agues, gout, "hoarse canker," and childbirth.

It was spring before he finally reached Connecticut. The roads were drying out but the ruts still held enough water to reflect the clear blue sky. He could hear the smallest stream long before he saw its rushing torrent flooding the emerald banks. And the fields and the hillsides were fair with the first fresh golden-green. The nearer he came home, the slower he walked. In spite of his hard-won maturity, something of a boy's shyness returned to delay his steps as he thought of the Leffingwells and the ordered life under their comfortable roof.

Jonathan did not approach the house from the road, but took the long pasture path that sloped up toward the orchard. Swinging through the stile, he saw between the gray trunks of the trees the flash of Time's sky-blue tammy petticoat. She was under the vergaloo pear tree, staring up into the branches that would soon break into soft white bloom. Beside her stood Fortune, his gray poll like pewter in the early morning sun. When they both turned, surprised at Jonathan's call, Time clapped her lean black hands to her turbaned head. It was a familiar gesture, and so were the bows that the old Negro made as he came toward the young man to greet him. And he accomplished these with no loss of grace, though he held aloft a forked stick from which drooped the iridescent bodies of several plump fish. Noticing these, Jonathan's grin widened and his heart at last acknowledged a delight in being home. There would be trout for breakfast!

If Jonathan's long absence had made no difference in Time or Fortune, the same could not be said of Nancy, Deborah, and Lucy. They were transformed. In fact, Lucy, although but nineteen, had acquired so gravely competent an air that but for the slenderness of her waist laced into its chintz gown, she might have been mistaken for a very sober matron. It was both natural and proper that Jonathan should fall in love with Lucy, and this he proceeded to do without the least delay on his own part or the slightest objection of others. They were married the following year, and set up their modest establishment in a small story-and-a-half house on the other side of Meeting House Rocks around the corner from the Green.

In those first twelve years of his marriage, between the end of one war and the beginning of another, Jonathan labored diligently not only to improve his own reputation and support his growing family, but also to further the dignity and the good report of his whole profession in the state. He was one of a group of physicians from the vicinity of Norwich that petitioned the Connecticut General Assembly for the right to regulate the practice of medicine. Previously the title of "doctor" or "professor of physic" had included lawyers with a knack for bonesetting, preachers whose parishes were in remote sections, Negro freedmen who had once served in physicians' households, and any goodwife with even the smallest knowledge of simples.

Jonathan went wherever he might be called, but his

keenest interest and his greatest success lay in those cases which demanded the utmost of his skillful hands. He developed a talent for removing gallstones and at the same time saving the life of his patient, a combination of miracles that impressed a clumsier man like Dr. Leffingwell as being something almost akin to magic. The older man was only too glad to surrender all such risks to his son-in-law, particularly as his own popularity and prosperity continued.

Dr. Leffingwell now made his calls in a chaise, an elegant affair with a yellow body and a red-morocco top, a startling, even scandalous, innovation for Norwich Town. Some considered this vehicle so worldly as to be sinful; others disliked the aristocratic pretensions of the coat of arms on the back. Jonathan thought it effeminate and continued himself to go about the countryside on his dependable mare, or in winter often using his "skaits" if his way took him along the river, or through meadows frozen over with a hard, unyielding glaze of snow.

In Jonathan's office there was a skeleton—all that remained of a Negro slave named Jock. At twilight, the thought of those glimmering bones would send terrified children scampering past the Adgate house, fearful of meeting Jock's ghost. The man had good reason to haunt the neighborhood, for he had been wretched both in life and in death. Jealous of the girl he was courting, he had attempted to shoot her, loading his gun with pieces of a pewter spoon instead of bullets. She was hit in the shoulder, but Jock never waited to see how badly. He ran off to a swamp, where he hid until hunger, fear, and remorse brought him home. Once in jail, some taunting boys came to his window and told him that his sweetheart was dead. He hanged himself in his cell, and his body was given to Jonathan for dissection.

At the time of the Revolution, Jonathan Adgate was approaching middle age. His children were still young, his practice, built up doggedly as well as by the help of some spectacular operations, had arrived at the point where it was called "respectable." He could easily have found good excuses under the circumstances for avoiding such active service as he had known in his independent youth in the earlier war. But the army had never lost its fascination for him. And Dr. Leffingwell, he thought, could be responsible for both his family and his practice, if necessary. So he set forth again, though this time not as an unknown and inexperienced boy, nor to travel so far away from home.

During the campaigns of 1776 he gained such distinction as a surgeon that the following spring he was made Surgeon General of the Eastern Department of the Hospital, with headquarters at Danbury. All the hospitals east of the Hudson came under his supervision, and although some of these were not in existence for long, there were a good many of them. At first he wrote, "My circuit visiting ye Different Hospitals is four hundred miles and upwards." Although later this distance was reduced, the journey still remained wearisome enough. Lame or feeble horses, even the difficulty of finding horses at all, constantly delayed him. Orders from superiors were more easily delivered than followed, as several letters indicated. One from Jonathan himself to the Director-General stated:

The hospitals you have directed me to attend are at the distance of two hundred miles or more in Circuit, travelling is very expensive. How am I to be supplied with horses and other necessary expenses, to perform this duty in rotation, is it my own expense or the publics? . . . Our troops are detached and sent to different places on or near the sea coast requesting our assistance at almost every place. However I shall endeavor to make all easy.

And later a young assistant in Boston, writing to Jonathan, showed in his turn the same uneasiness and bewilderment:

Sir,

Doctor Foster's Ill state of Health has obliged him to make a Journey to the Eastward. he has desired me Inform you that he is in Hourly expectation of a sum of moneys arriving from Philadelphia; as soon as it arrives he has Ordered me to Purchase such articles as will be Immediately wanting, and to repair to New Port, and New London, and give you all the assistance that lays in my power. Mr. Bright is Still here and cant go forward for the Want of Money to defray his travelling expenses. I have made out to collect a Small Supply of Tea, chocolate, loaf & Brown Sugar on Credit, which shall be sent forward to Doctor Adams at Tivertown as soon as the Quartermaster can furnish a team. I have called upon him three times today, & urged the Necessity of having the stores sent forward. he has promised me his Assistance as soon as it lays in his power. I hope you will do me the Justise to believe, that as soon as the money arrives, No time shall be lost. . . . With respect to Medicines, Bandages, etc. I have informed Doctor Adams that there is a large supply in the packages at Providence, and have requested him to order some careful Person that he can confide in, to select out such articles as may be wanting for Immediate Use.

That last sentence reveals what was perhaps the worst difficulty of all. If money and supplies were both woefully lacking, so too were "careful Persons" in whom the doctors could "confide." Apparently constant pilfering went on from the stores of tea, coffee, and sugar. In December 1778, Jonathan received a long report from the senior surgeon in Danbury, which not only mentioned such theft but also described other conditions there very vividly.

> Tea, coffee, sugar, etc, are given to the care of the orderly man, and if the orderly men chance to be possessed of honesty and humanity, the patients for whom they are prescribed get them: but this is running a needless risque, and giving unnecessary opportunity to embezzle; for if there were some faithful humane person to whom these articles might be intrusted, they would be made up properly and exhibited to the patients as their several situations required. . . . It affects one very disagreeably, and if humanity is not out of the question it will be called forth and exercised; to go into the hospital on the hill in Danbury and to see the situation of those unhappy people whose fortune it is to be sent there; frequently destitute of firing unless taken from the fences (and then you frequently hear complaints from the owners) without vegetables, often without straw, and not clean as they would be were people appointed to keep them so; and the most ill patients not supplied with drinks and diet, suitable to their exigencies, private soldiers who are in common the orderlys and nurses cannot be depended on, and indeed ought not on so important occassion on which depends the life of many a brave soldier.

There would be petty troubles sometimes among the doctors, too. One gentleman had bought between three and four hundredweight of cathartic salts with the idea of selling exclusively to the hospital. He had been encouraged in this project by one of the Director General's assistants, who in the end, however, bought a cheaper supply elsewhere. This caused "bickering" between them, and a long, plaintive letter to Jonathan from the disappointed speculator, claiming the superiority of his own salts, offering now to sell at cost, and asking Jonathan "to direct in his behalf."

The hospitals in some towns were maintained longer than in others. They would be discontinued as the troops moved, and the equipment and the medical officers ordered to a new station. In such instances, Jonathan's directions were brisk and definite:

Dear Sir

You will proceed forthwith to Majr. Genl. Heaths Headquarters at or near ye Highland with Dr. Vinal of Gardner to your Assistance you will Order a Waggon with two able Horses to Attend you with every kind of Chyrurgical Apparatus, Instruments, Bandages, old Linnen, &c. &c. Such quantities of Medicines as Necessary in Case of Action and Call on Capt. Berian for such sums of moneys and refreshments as equal to Support a Tour of this kind when you arrive there wait on the Genl. Directiam, make punctual weekly reports of your Medical Attendance, keep Accurate Accts. of the expenditures of Moneys etc that at ye close of ye Tour there may be a Settlement. . . . Dear Sir, I wish you Success . . .

The hospital in Hartford was one of those which lasted only a few months, though it was necessary enough at the time that Jonathan sent his order:

Collect the Sick and Wounded under ye Command of Majr. Genl. Putnam and all the straggling sick of the Continental Army into some Suitable place for their reception, for which apply to ye Genl. for Assistance & Orders for Large warm and Comfortable Houses for their accomodation.

So he continued through these years, riding endlessly over the long lonesome roads, either by himself on some weary horse or with companions in a rough cart that held his big cedar-lined trunk full of medicines, instruments, and bandages. And his destination was always monotonously the same—some scene of suffering and distress where other doctors waited for him with their discouraging reports, complaints, and demands.

Meanwhile, in Norwich Town Jonathan's wife Lucy, their children, and old Dr. Leffingwell carried on as best they could. Norwich, however, being an inland and industrial town, survived the whole war far less disastrously than her neighbor city, New London, at the mouth of the river. At least her small industries and businesses did not cease to function entirely, though prices were strictly regulated, either by acts of the Assembly or by the town selectmen. One could still buy the best "silver-plaited" coat buttons for six shillings per dozen, ivory small-tooth combs for from one to five shillings, a quart pewter pot for six shillings fivepence, and yard-wide checked flannel or linen for five shillings. The coopers went on turning out their hogsheads, barrels, and tierces; the stocking mill and the tape mill, the tanners, the saddlers, and others, did not lack for trade. The householders went without wheat, salt, and molasses, although they managed to find even those when gifts were asked for the soldiers or the sick. But rice, potatoes, chocolate, and spices could be bought, and mutton and veal as well as game and "store swine"; fresh bass, perch, and river oysters were on sale at the Landing. At either of the two taverns hungry wayfarers could obtain "a meal of victuals" for one shilling and ninepence. There was a variety of beverages for the thirsty, including a mug of flip or toddy flavored with

New England rum, or with West Indian rum if one cared to pay the extra shilling.

Numerous prosperous refugees from Boston, Newport, and other cities came to Norwich for the duration of the war, one gentleman causing quite a flurry when he arrived in a coach with outriders, and again when he departed with his baby daughter carried in a basket strapped to the head of an Indian runner. Prisoners of war, occasionally in large numbers, were brought and held there, and once or twice some Tory or "grumbletonian" would be the center of an angrily excited mob. The town, however, like most others in Connecticut, stood solidly for patriotism under the leadership of Governor Trumbull. The calls for soldiers and for their supplies were answered swiftly and without complaint. Everyone contributed actual money for the army, as well as gifts of cheese, sugar corn, rice, and other commodities. The women gathered at different houses to make stockings, shirts, and mittens, or to bring buff caps, rifle frocks, overalls, and shoes.

Even little girls like Felicity, Jonathan Adgate's daughter, attended these meetings, so that the soldiers and their needs became a commonplace to her. She was accustomed to the sight of the town militia, and in addition detachments of the Continental Army often passed through the town, sometimes camping there for a night or two. Even more exciting were the few glimpses that she had of French officers, on their way through to Newport or riding down from winter quarters at Lebanon to be entertained and feasted at the big white Huntington house beyond the Green. In comparison with the ill-clad and often emaciated Continentals, these glittering foreigners with plumes in their hats and colored facings on their white coats dashed into the town like godlike creatures from some other star.

Von Steuben, Pulaski, De Fersen, De Lauzun—with all such difficult syllables the tongues of the townspeople struggled, but Lafayette was the one magical name that everyone knew and used indiscriminately for all these apparitions of splendor. It was he, supposedly, who came one time with two thousand of his countrymen for a night's encampment and who before leaving drew up his soldiers in three sides of a hollow square while at his courteous invitation the pastor from the meetinghouse (the "temple," the Frenchmen called it) bestowed a Protestant blessing on these Catholic troops.

Felicity, with her sisters and brothers, was one who watched this spectacle, open-mouthed, and later stood on the roadside while the troops passed out of town. They fell into line and marched with a precision unbelievable to those who hitherto had seen only their own small training bands on the Green, where the drilling, though spirited enough, was awkward, and the commands—such as "Blow off the loose corns" and "Shoulder-hoo!"—were more according to local than to strictly martial traditions. Behind the Frenchmen went their baggage wagons drawn by oxen or horses, or sometimes by both, and the carts, with special guards, bearing the kegs of silver money. The whole pageant was strange enough for the simple people of Norwich Town, but stranger still were the reports from other parts of Connecticut that these brave, lace-trimmed allies, either through innocence or through oddity, put young tobacco leaves in their salad and frogs' legs in their soup.

Years later in New York, grown-up Felicity, hearing her father's pen eternally scratching away at his indignant epistles, remembered these times and these events. Sometimes, homesick for Connecticut, she took the Norwich packet and went back for a visit, but Jonathan never went with her. He was through with it for good and all. He did not find the prosperous practice that he had hoped for in New York, however. Perhaps his aging hands had lost their earlier swift skill, or there were too many other and less provincial physicians now in the city. Certainly most of the entries in his account book were for the simplest kinds of ministrations to such humble people as his "candleman," his "coffeeman," "a woman in Bedlow St.," or "a man on sloop Jay." He often received discreet little notes of introduction, which had evidently been preceded by cautious conversations:

"Sir, the bearer, Mr. Wood, is the young Gentleman I described to you last evening, who wishes medical assistance."

But one writer, more outspoken, said: "The young gentleman bearer of this is a particular friend of mine, and being afflicted with a severe attack of the venereal, I must claim your special care of him for his speedy relief. I shall depend upon you keeping it secret." The number of cases of such "young gentlemen" recorded by Jonathan was equaled only by that of the "lying-in" patients. Almost any week, he jotted down something like the following:

"Van Horn; to a visit in the night—obstetricating his wife."

People from Connecticut still wrote to him beseeching him to come to them in crises where surgical skill was needed. Sometimes they merely wanted a written opinion, like a man from Wallingford who appeared to be sadly afflicted with abscesses or sores of some kind. To his request Jonathan replied with a detailed list of instructions, beginning with the comment that the patient's "unhappy, diseased situation must be left much to nature's recovering principle," proceeding to directions for "compresses wet in a strong decoction of white oak bark, Brandy and salt. . . . Bark, steel and good wine internally, porter etc. etc. . . . a decoction of the woods in lime water, such as lignum vitae chips, liquorish, sarsparilla, saxafrax roots . . . a wine glass at a time . . . the most nutritious diet —sometime one thing and sometime another . . . shell-fish, oysters etc. out of the shell raw, as a laxative and corrector."

Sometimes Jonathan received odd payments for his services, such as "two shadd and a piece of Haulabud fish." Once his patient handed him an original poem, which promised that his "Asculapiun wisdom" would be repaid by everything from "Heaven itself" to "sweet benevolence," but failed to mention even the hope of the smallest fee.

The burden of his poverty was lifted to some extent in 1808, when the Government settled part of his claim, as they had done for others in the General Hospital. About that time too, after almost seven years of letter-writing, he received his appointment to re-enter the army. He had set his heart on this shortly after his arrival in New York, in spite of all his bitterness resulting from the Revolution. Once more he found himself with troops at Fort Columbus on Governors Island. From there he continued to write, deploring the confusion that he found, the lack of supplies, and criticizing the young doctors with ever increasing severity. He complained that "we are totally destitute of stores, save a little durty molasses, and damaged Black teas, a jubble of refuse medicine, nobody knows what, left here by the troops last fall." When he wrote to the "purveyor" for new supplies, he sometimes mingled his lists of desired articles with loyal statements about those under his care:

> . . . white Vitriol, Nitric & Muriatic acids, Manna flake, Myrrh, and every other article allowed, especially flannel, muslin, lint. we are a worthy sett of people posted on our frontiers for the defense of our country, and not only love but deserve everything good. In addition one doz. large mouth specie Bottles, Glass stoppers, or lacur'd Covers.

And he stormed constantly about the failings and the pretensions—as he considered the new methods—of the rising generation. Once in a report he scornfully alluded to a young surgeon as "of no use here or anywhere—a simple Cypher." One youth he scolded unmercifully in a series of letters, finally saying, "You have the least manners I ever saw belonging to education . . . the words insulting and ungentlemanlike will apply best to your shineing character; enough of this folly, I say enough. Amen."

Meanwhile he went about his own duties conscientiously and exhaustively, writing proudly to one friend,

"I remain the same steady old man at public duty every day." Nevertheless, one cannot help wondering whether not only the old man's hands, but also his judgment, had begun to fail him grievously. Earlier in his career, perhaps one Joseph Jones would not have received his discharge:

> I have paid a ready attention to the case of Joseph Jones, a soldier of Lieut. Goodale's party, or detachment, and find by correct information, that he is subject to Epileptic fitts, and has been for a number of years, and one paroxism, since on this island, he has cut one of his great toes off, at present lame and unfitt for the duties of a Soldier, under all circumstances I think it better to discharge him.

Joseph Jones's release from serving his country must have inspired his fellows, for in a report of sixty-nine invalids sent in by Jonathan, many of them were addicted to "fitts."

In spite of his share in this third war, Jonathan was not contented. Still looking to the future, he snatched up his pen and started another campaign in his own behalf to procure a regular appointment on "the peace establishment." This would mean a surgeon's commission at Fort Columbus, where he now hoped to remain for the rest of his life. And eventually it was arranged for; it was promised him; it would reach him "in a few days," wrote the Chief Clerk of the War Department in 1813.

But the appointment never came. All through the next year, and until his death in the following winter, his letters flowed from him in a constant stream. Many an evening there he sat, in his shabby damask dressing-gown, his worn velvet skull cap slightly askew, the quiet flames from the tall candlestand at his elbow casting shadows across his crotchety, tired old face, writing and writing his ignored letters. Sometimes they were dignified in tone, sometimes reproachful and wistful, often almost imploring or even close to despair.

If there is any difficulty why my commission is not Issued, pray tell me what it is. . . . Appear for me once more. . . . I was induced to get me a regimental uniform dress, which I dare not appear in until I have my commission. . . . Where the Secty. of War is I don't know. I have wrote to him twice and never heard from him. I ought to beware of the third time. . . . It is an unhappy situation to be in the dark. . . . I have been wronged and neglected somewhere.

CHAPTER VIII

TRACY HOYT AND FELICITY

WHEN Jonathan Adgate married Lucy Leffingwell, Tracy Hoyt was just enough younger to be coming to Norwich as a young lawyer to attend the court. He liked to call at the yellow house evenings to sit around the fire with Dr. Leffingwell and his wife and the two unmarried daughters, Nancy and Deborah. Sometimes Jonathan and Lucy were there too. Apples and nuts would be passed around in the polished pewter dish, and in frosty weather Fortune, his black face beaming with sociability, always bobbed in bearing mugs of cider sprinkled with red pepper.

Most people believed that Tracy was courting either Nancy or Deborah. But their fair hair, calm faces, and decorous ways attracted only his mildly admiring eye. His heart had been touched already—even a little scorched—by someone darker and more dangerous down the river nearer home. What really drew Tracy Hoyt to this hospitable hearth most of all, though nobody guessed it, was the odd figure of Ebenezer Leffingwell, the Doctor's younger brother. Ebenezer was something of a ne'er-do-well, a charming dreamer who played the fiddle. He would be gone for months at a time, none knew where, to return out at elbow and down at heel if not coatless and barefoot, but sure of a welcome from the family of his prosperous brother.

All kinds of rumors arose around the vagrant Ebenzer. The Leffingwell girls liked best that legend which related how he had walked home from the rocky caves of Wawecus Hill one summer afternoon, down the road, over the bridge, and through the town, playing some weird and solemn dance that nobody had ever heard before. Behind him, all the way, curving through leaves, pebbles, and dust, slid a huge rattlesnake, his flat head lifted a little, yearningly, and swaying in a bemused, ecstatic trance. Ebenezer would not deny the tale; he only smiled vaguely when it was mentioned.

Now Tracy Hoyt loved a tune. He himself played the flute, and a delicately sweet and satisfying instrument he always thought it, except on those evenings when Ebenezer, leaning toward the firelight from a corner of the settle, tucked his fiddle under his narrow, gypsyish chin and drew the bow across the strings. Such music, so unlike his own thin, respectable piping, sometimes almost made Tracy cry, and at other times scared him. To be swept away into a world of secret and shivery delight, where anything might happen, disconcerted a young man who fancied himself humorously detached from all the moods and passions. Perhaps on that morning when, astonished and rueful, he awoke to find himself the spouse of Miranda Wheeler, he may have seemed to hear a faraway aching and mocking music to remind him, distressingly at such a moment, that sometimes even the heart of a clever lawyer is capable of the most treacherous tricks.

Certainly he had never meant to marry Miranda. A fine lady, not a fine animal, was what he had always imagined as the companion of his future, when he had risen in the world and enriched himself and become the well-mannered and well-living gentleman that he intended to be. Yet here he was, housed forever with this stormy, tropical creature. But he tried to make the best of it, and particularly to forget that mystery which had followed Miranda from childhood, that persistent malicious whispering that her father was not the staid little ship's carpenter Matthew Wheeler, but instead someone described at his most innocent as a man from Guadeloupe, but usually as the blackest of characters with gold rings dangling from his ears and a smile as evil as the blade of a knife.

Miranda's own nature seemed to verify such tales, for it was the battlefield for conflicting forces. She could scream at poor Tracy like a fishwife, using a vocabulary that raised every hair on his smooth blond head, or she could speak to him in a voice so seductively and passionately tender that, struggle as he might, the blood in his veins turned slowly to streams of honeyed fire. Sometimes, enduring the whole range of emotions, all the way from simple exasperation to cruel heartbreak, he would meditate bitterly on the power of a shrewish woman, and begin to wish that he had been born in an earlier day when he could have condemned Miranda to the ducking-stool and silenced her wicked tongue beneath the brackish waters of the harbor. However, after the birth of the two of their children who lived, Christopher and Betsey, their mutual enraging and inflaming became less violent. Tracy could forgive Miranda much for the sake of the fair rosy son whose blue eyes reflected the amused glance of his own, and the gentle little daughter whose dark curls clustering on her head and delightful tiptilted nose gave her such a gay, almost elfin, air.

As for Miranda, she surprised even herself by her fierce maternal pride and her longing to have such beautiful children return her devotion in full measure. But she was never quite as subdued as her portrait suggested when Tracy had it painted by a traveling artist who came to New London during a prosperous winter. Although he persuaded her to wear her most genteel dress of pale-blue lutestring, a silver ribbon binding her dark hair, and to sit erect with her hands sedately folded, the result remained essentially Miranda. There she sat, dressed and posed like a lady; but the full lower lip was as sensuous as ever and the black eyes still smoldered.

Through all these years, in sullenness, cold rage, or false content, Tracy continued to play his flute. Summer evenings, on a wooden bench under an apple tree he sat by himself listening to his own sweet, lonely little airs—

"Green Grow the Rushes O" . . . "Handsome Charming Will" . . . "My Lodging Is on the Cold Ground" . . . "If 'Tis Joy to Wound a Lover." He had the notes all copied out in a small notebook, but he seldom studied them. And he would go on playing even after dusk had descended over the sunset-tinted harbor, the cluster of houses over on the Groton shore, and the tall-masted ships resting so quietly in the clear, untroubled water.

Sometimes Tracy paused, and with his flute on his knee gazed out speculatively at the rigging of those ships, delicate as cobwebs in the darkening air. Most of them he knew well, and their owners and their masters. Such men often called on the law, and some part of Tracy's small prosperity could be attributed to their needs and dilemmas. The captains were friendly and often brought him gifts, Valencia oranges or bottles of Canary or Madeira wine, or perhaps a painted fan or a damask tablecloth for Miranda, and once a large green porcelain jar, its sides covered with yellow and rose-colored flowers and figures of fantastic creatures. Tracy coveted choice possessions, and he became more and more exacting in his tastes.

During the Revolution it was not surprising that the fastidious, flute-playing, comfort-loving Tracy found little difficulty in persuading himself that he would make an abominable soldier. Unlike that handsome young schoolmaster who for a short time had taught the New London children, Tracy would have regretted it very much indeed if he had had to lose even his one life for his country. He was awkward with guns and squeamish about blood, always persuading someone else to shoot his game for him, but now he felt forced to buy a brace of pistols, which he kept in the top of his secretary. He conscientiously examined them every so often, but always late at night, by himself, with a forlorn and helpless smile.

If Tracy was not a fighter, neither was he a Tory, and he went to work quite cheerfully with others in the town on the Committee of Correspondence, issuing declarations and resolutions and handling a mass of intercolony messages concerning the progress of the war in other sections. These were mostly dreary tasks, with interludes of anxious excitement when a rider on a sweating horse brought in some warning of danger. From Guilford came such a message in 1777, dated July 19, "ten o'clock at night."

Sirs,

I have this moment received the following by express from Generl. Silliman. Should be glad you send it along the Seashore to the Eastermost Towns in this State—

"Sir,

By Express from Col. Mead at Horseneck who came away last night I am informed that they discovered Forty Sail of the Front of the Enemy's Fleet from New York standing Eastward. 25 of them are now in sight of my house off of Norwalk standing directly for this town. I expect they will land here before night. I have to entreat you immediately to march your Brigade to our assistance, this I think is by all means necessary for even if they should pass us I don't think they will New Haven, so that you will be in the greater Readiness to Receive them which I think is by all means necessary. I think it will be best to Dispatch this Intelligence along the Towns Eastward as far as this State reaches—

I am Sir Yours Obtl,
"G. Sellick Silliman."

The next day at seven o'clock in the evening Tracy and another member of the committee set their signatures to this comment written on the back of the letter:

> The Within is a Copy of a Letter Forwarded to the Commanding Officer at this place—About Forty Sail have just past the Harbour and are still standing Eastward suppose as for Newport by their Course.

And beneath this the final word was added by the commanding officer, addressed to his Major General:

> I think it my Duty to Inform your Honnour that I sent the above Intelligence about a Hour past to his Excelency Gov. Trumbull the ships have now passd the Harbour I conclude for Newport as Capt Niles is this minute arrivd after being chased who has a Deserter on Board who says they are Victualling Ships bound home. . . . I now send this to prevent any needless alarm. . . .

New London was frightened in this same way again and again. Her inhabitants, though always uneasy, grew accustomed to the sight of enemy vessels bearing down on the mouth of the river, sometimes to anchor watchfully near, at other times swerving away again to Fisher's Island, where once they carried off over a thousand of Mr. Brown's sheep, or farther to Plum Island and Gardiner's Island, sometimes after provisions, sometimes recruiting. Over and over the New Londoners prepared for an attack, ringing the bells, firing the alarm guns, sending away the women and children, packing up valuables and records and hiding them. Messengers would speed away inland calling out the militia from the near-by Connecticut towns, sometimes even from Massachusetts. Then the danger would pass, and the waters of the Sound seem innocently, even mockingly, empty and blue.

Tracy had seen everything in the streets of his town except the British soldiers. He had seen riots between recruiting privateersmen, townspeople, and militia; houses, even of friends, ruthlessly entered and searched for evidences of the despised "Long Island trading"; men returned from the prison ships so disfigured and wasted that many of them died on the roads or, babbling with fever, tried to beg their way to homes that they could only dimly remember. But the actual ominous color of the enemy's coat he had not seen until that September day in 1781 when, for once unsuspecting and unprepared, the town awoke to find the King's men swarming on the shore.

By dawn the little streets were full of the sounds of flying feet and women's sharp cries, the low rumble of laden carts, with occasionally the staccato beat of a galloping horse or one more dully jogging along to the ludicrous accompaniment of banging pots and kettles tied to the saddle. Here and there in the crowd a cluster of white-faced children, holding each other's hands, ran silently toward the shelter of the woods or, piteously obedient to their lost and scattered elders, fled for the Norwich road. Clouds of dust rose and hung transparently in the still late-summer air. And later on another cloud, denser and uglier than the dust, rose in columns from the burning river front to spread over the abandoned town.

Tracy had heard the guns in the night, but the signal was confused and he could not be certain whether it meant an attack or the announcement of another prize brought in by privateers. He could not believe that now, after all these years of false alarms and futile rehearsals, the disaster had actually arrived. That it did not descend upon him, upon all of them, brutally in the dark was, as he learned afterward, because of "Providence." Providence, riding the wind, had shifted it so that it came out of the north and, blowing down the river, held the ships offshore. Even Benedict Arnold, who led the British on this raid and who had planned it so cleverly, had forgotten to include any possibly treacherous Providence in his calculations. But with the daylight even the fickle wind turned again to side with the redcoats against the town.

Tracy's first thought was to get his family out of the house and away. Since they must leave at once and on foot, he saw no reason for waiting to conceal any valuables, or to try to carry anything with them except money and a little food. They must not hope to reach Norwich, fourteen miles away, but to find shelter in some farm back on the hills. But Miranda as usual lifted up her voice protesting. Even against the vast murmur and shuffle of desperation and terror rising throughout the whole town, the clamor of men in the harbor weighing anchor and lifting sail, the occasional dull pounding of a gun—even, finally, against that sound which, though still distant, was piercing and savage, the enemy's advancing fife and drum—even against all that Miranda raised her obstinate and indignant voice. She had no intention of surrendering everything to the British without a struggle—nor for that matter to Tracy either. So it was that, at last angrily acquiescent, he rushed out into the garden and dug a hole in some loose earth under the apple tree. Into it he lowered the big green porcelain jar, which Miranda filled with some cherished pieces of silver and jewelry. They had just finished smoothing the earth again when tiny Betsey came out of the house crying. Christopher had left her. Christopher had run away.

Tracy's remembrance of what had happened after that was a frantic confusion. But he knew that by force he held the agonized Miranda from following blindly after her son, and convinced her that she must get away with Betsey while he remained to search for the boy. Fortunately he found places for them on a neighbor's cart. Miranda, disheveled and woebegone, sat on a heap of goods tied up in a sheet and turned her back on him. But Betsey, too small to understand the confusion, smiled quite happily now at the prospect of a ride in a cart and continued to wave to her father as she was jolted away.

Tracy stood at the edge of the road, hatless, coatless, and breathless, wondering where on earth to look first for a mischievous, lively little son who had vanished so fearlessly into what seemed like the end of the world. Hoping the boy had followed the crowd in their flight, he turned in that direction for a while. It was not for some time, when he was a long way from home, that he remembered his pistols, so prudently bought against just such an occasion as this. He had left them behind him, safely reposing in the top of his secretary. Feeling more than a little foolish and thinking to return for them later, he continued on his search.

He did not once see Christopher throughout the day, or hear of him. By early afternoon he, with dozens of other scattered, leaderless, and bewildered citizens, had been driven in every direction, as panic-stricken as animals before the advance of trained huntsmen. Those who had guns crouched behind walls or trees, determined to send a few shots at least at those hateful invaders who marched so briskly here and there through the forsaken town, their lines in perfect order, the white straps crossing their red breasts and backs with such smart neatness, their silver buttons and their bayonets agleam. Once, from a thicket on a hilltop where he paused for a moment panting, Tracy looked down toward the harbor and saw what seemed like thousands of those red-coated demons darting in and out of the spreading smoke. The whole river front was on fire, docks and warehouses bright with flame. A ship burnt down to its hull broke loose and, smoldering, drifted out into the river, trailing dull reflections.

Toward evening Tracy learned from an old Negro—the servant of a friend—who came trudging down the Norwich road that Miranda and Betsey were safe at the Miller farm. The place was full of people, he said, and the Millers had fed them all as long as their stores lasted with milk and cheese and porringers of beans. Satisfied of their safety, but not daring to face Miranda without news of Christopher, Tracy turned back once more toward the town. Against the darkening sky rose a sullen glare, and black clouds trailed across the first stars. With no clear idea as to just why he did so, but somehow now too weary, hungry, and forlorn to take any other except the familiar way, come what might, he went toward home.

But home was only a fiery pit in the ground, with flames still licking over its edges. The smoke tasted bitter in his mouth and smarted in his eyes, already flowing with angry tears. The light flickering this way and that threw a rosy shaft down the long garden path to the apple tree. The wooden bench had been spared, and on it, blinking and rather drowsily munching an apple, sat Christopher. His face and arms were covered with dirt and soot, his breeches spotted and smelling of an extraordinary combination of rum and grease, and the whole front of his shirt bore stains that, though now dried, were dark and unmistakable. But it was only English blood, he explained to his father; it had spurted out on him when he had tried to help an old man who was half carrying, half dragging a wounded soldier into an empty house.

Christopher had been in and out of dozens of empty houses. In one he had found a great feast spread forth upon a long table—meats, cakes, and wines—as though guests had been expected, though not a soul remained to greet them. But he had found the most excitement down near a warehouse where the redcoats were breaking up hogsheads and pouring the contents into the street. It was there that, running, he had stumbled over a pile of coffee and fallen headlong into the gutter, which was running with rum, sugar, and melting butter.

Tracy and his son spent that night in a barn which had escaped the fire. Christopher laid himself down on a pile of hay on the floor and instantly fell asleep. But Tracy sat for a time in the open door staring into the night, which was still aglow with the ashes of the town. After all, he was alive, and his family too. Even part of their possessions had been saved, for long ago they had left a few things in Norwich, and he felt sure the big jar still lay buried beneath the apple tree. Yes, they were lucky. He had acknowledged that even before he saw lights moving in and around the fort across the river on the Groton hillside and knew that they were carried by women who were searching for their dead.

Although years after the end of the war many of the New London homes were still in ruins, most of the city had been rebuilt. The ships were again sailing, not only for the West Indies but for European ports. And on August 27, 1788, the *New London Gazette* published the following announcement: "Thomas Allen's marine list commences on a new hope, the Federal Constitution."

Perhaps Tracy would not have stepped around so energetically if there had been no Miranda to goad him into activity. But she had no intention of remaining uncomfortably in the houses of others any longer than was strictly necessary. Their second home arose over the ruins of the first. She brought down her possessions that had been left in Norwich, among them her own portrait, which she rehung over the new mantelpiece. The green porcelain jar shone more lustrously than ever now that it had the additional dignity of a legend.

Before long Tracy was sitting under the apple tree experimenting with a new flute. And his glance, wandering over the harbor, found that even there too the ships had a novelty to offer, a curious craft designed by a man ten miles up the river, built almost entirely of plank and called a "snow." She was very graceful and swift, and so light that once in a storm she had sailed airily over a sandy point and stranded herself among the trees of an orchard. None the worse for her landfaring adventure, she departed for Ireland the following month. Her real name was *The*

Lady Strange, though people usually spoke of her as *The Balloon.*

Tracy's children grew into a young man and a young woman. He had some trouble for a while with the boy, who wanted to go to sea instead of settling down respectably to the practice of the law. Betsey was no trouble to anyone. As in childhood, the dark curls clustered enchantingly on her head, and though her black eyes were often serious, her face could never really seem pensive because of the utter frivolity of the small nose with its turned-up end. Often Tracy sadly reflected that soon they would have lives of their own, and he would be left to wrangle with Miranda through old age as best he might.

One summer he had been to New York and, returning on the packet, arrived in New London on a sultry evening late in August. He had been gone about three weeks, and had heard from home just once, from Miranda. Her letter complained of the continuing, unbearable heat, and ended with the following melancholy report: "Cousin Thomas has been for some days quite sick, and is still very unwell. There has been much sickness in the lower part of the town. You have I presume heard of the death of Captain Lathrop. His loss is very much regretted." However, she added that they themselves were "in tolerable health." Tracy tried not to associate her dismal news with the fact that an epidemic of yellow fever was then raging in New York. But when he boarded the packet he learned that the same dread disease had spread to New London. There had been many deaths there during the last few days, the captain told him, and frightened people were leaving the town in great numbers.

Certainly as he walked away from the dock toward home the streets were unusually empty. He seemed to be almost the only human being abroad, and his steps resounded mournfully in the silence. The one other figure that he saw ahead of him was that of an old woman who in spite of the heat was closely muffled in the folds of a shawl. As he approached her, she quickened her pace so hastily that she stumbled and, starting to run, disappeared into the dusk around a corner. Scarcely a house showed even the dimmest of lights, and there were no voices anywhere. Yet Tracy felt sure that through the cracks of shutters he was occasionally watched as he passed.

He shivered slightly even while the sweat trickled down his face. And he could not help pausing for a moment to turn and look back along the way he had come. A mosquito whined and pranced close to his eyes and, brushing it away, he saw now, in the waning silver light, something that he had not noticed before. Some of the doors were marked with a white cross. When he reached his own door, it was not yet too dark to see that there also the same sign warned of evil danger within.

Tracy entered his house trembling, as if he were a marauder in a strange place, not a man crossing the threshold of what had always been his own safe home. The shadowy staircase confronted him, and the tall, black oblongs of the doorways on either side of the hall were menacing in their emptiness. Of course the servants had run away. But then, did not friends, relatives, physicians even, flee before so terrifying a sickness as this? Perhaps after all the family had gone in time, escaped to some refuge in another town.

But it was useless to try to deceive himself against that one overwhelming presence which his senses had acknowledged long before he did—the faint, sour smell of vinegar mingled with another more penetrating and poisonous odor. Finally he forced himself to light a candle and slowly go upstairs. He went to the door of Miranda's room, which stood half-closed, and pushed it open. Miranda and Betsey were huddled, half-clad, amid a confusion of stained pillows and cloths on the big four-post bed. Near them on the floor the body of Christopher sprawled across a disordered heap of bedclothes that he had dragged in from some other room.

It was evident that the three, forsaken by all who might have helped them, had crawled into this one room to be together, if only to suffer and to give each other what aid and comfort they could as long as any hope or any life remained. Shutting out Tracy forever, they lay there, not only united in death but because of their particular death sharing an additional terrible estrangement from the living. Even Betsey, whose exquisite beauty he had loved so dearly, whose graciousness and gentleness had become so precious and intimate a part of his days—even she too disloyally concealed herself beneath a discolored and loathsome mask.

It was not until the fall that the stricken town saw the last of its pitiful victims put into the earth. Tracy's family was only one of many to vanish as though they had never existed, for unlike the decent burial ordinarily accorded to the dead, these were stealthily and hastily sealed up in their graves by those who were almost too terrified to mourn.

Tracy was not a deeply religious man, yet he could admire those among his similarly bereaved friends—particularly the women—who tried to offer him earnestly pious consolation. Mrs. Saltonstall, the wife of another lawyer in New London, had been widowed during the epidemic, and she wrote Tracy a note of condolence in a style quite worthy of her serious and stately character. He had always respected her, and he kept her note, which he found himself often rereading as he sat alone in a house that had now become unbearably peaceful. Finally he could even fancy that she sat beside him, and that it was actually her deep, placid voice which said to him:

> The dealings of Providence to us mortals of such limited capacities are truly mysterious and trying—but let none of us doubt that there is a God in Israel—and pray let all of us try to believe that it is our duty calmly to submit to his dispensations without murmur or complaint. The human heart, however, is constituted of such tender and susceptible materials that for a time it revolts and becomes wretched at the parting scene—but blessed is God—a way has been provided, by which, in the course of Time, we are kindly relieved of the indescribable anguish consquent on these heart-rending scenes—

And shortly after the turn of the century Tracy's dream of that comfortable female figure seated soothingly beside him in the firelight became a reality.

His second marriage proved to be all that the first had not been. Lydia Saltonstall was well bred, well mannered, and well dowered. Miranda's tempestuous memory was eclipsed as completely as a wind-blown flame is quenched by a polished silver snuffer. If Lydia's beaked, high-colored face was more aristocratic than beautiful, her figure more massive than graceful, at least she could lay claim to perfect suitability as the wife of a man who had now become a judge. Tracy stepped out quite pompously with so splendidly decorous a matron on his arm.

However, this espousal, though for the most part serenely satisfactory, did not entirely lack moments of agitation. There was, for instance, the question of the flute. Lydia considered none of the arts respectable, and a "music man" had no associations in her mind except as some coarse fellow who accompanied strolling players or Italian rope-dancers, or who played for a low entertainer like Clumsy the Clown, who, blindfolded, danced a hornpipe over fifteen eggs. But no gentleman—and certainly no judge—should frivol with such inferior pursuits. So Tracy, without argument, locked the flute away in a drawer.

There were, too, his books, which Lydia regarded as being mostly of an "infidel character." There, however, he stood his ground, and though she never passed the volumes without a glance of grave disapproval, she left them alone.

Also Tracy's heart contracted ever so slightly when for the first time he discovered that the miniatures of his curly-haired little Betsey and his fair, smiling son had been set aside in a dark corner. But he offered no rebuke. Certainly he never inquired what had become of Miranda's portrait. And after a while he had his own painted, seated in one of Lydia's Chippendale chairs, in a fine blue coat, an immaculate ruffle under his chin and a quill pen on a table beside him. If the eyes that looked out over the room were a little cynical, a little weary perhaps, that was after all only because the painter considered that he had put in the proper expression for a legal gentleman to have.

Lydia was by no means youthful, yet she had a solemn conception of the whole duty of a wife. She proceeded to present Tracy with a daughter and a son as soon as possible, though not too hastily to be compatible with gentility. It may have been this very conscientiousness which shortened her life, for at the end of seven years Tracy found himself once more a widower. He was now sixty-two, not an age at which it is comfortable to face the future with two small children without the help of some good-natured woman. Quite deliberately he began to look around him for just such a person, and in this unromantic fashion he found his way to Felicity.

It would not seem as though success in any startling degree would result from a marriage between an elderly man whose mood was mostly one of desperation and a middle-aged spinster who, after a few shabby years in New York, hankered for a comfortable home in Connecticut. Yet one day in the presence of a visitor Tracy paid his last wife a graceful compliment. Surveying her with a smile, which one lifted eyebrow tinged with only the faintest of ironical implications, he said:

"I lived in Hell with my first wife. I arrived upon the surface of the earth with my second. Now I am in Heaven with my third."

Felicity's responsibilities might well have taxed the resourcefulness of an angel, for in addition to a husband old enough to be her father, and two stepchildren, Abigail and Joshua, aged six and eight, she very soon blossomed into a mother herself. Instead of being thrown into consternation and distress by this unforeseen event (so unseasonable for her forty years!), she remained full of vigor and cheerfulness.

The infant boy Turner, whose shapely head covered only with the lightest of down Tracy thought surely denoted a good, judicial brain, provided them all with an object of mutual pride and delight. Abigail from the very first hovered constantly and maternally near the baby. She was a pudgy, rather pop-eyed child who breathed earnestly and hard over every task, whether it was gently rocking the cradle or copying out verses in her "Day-Book" in a painstaking hand. She was a more dutiful child than Joshua, who always remained something of an enigma to Felicity. If he had been Miranda's son, his alternating fits of hilarity and melancholy might have seemed naturally bestowed. But for the staid Lydia to have produced so moody and incalculable a nature puzzled both Felicity and his father.

Most of Tracy's puzzling, however, during these last few years of his life were concentrated on Felicity herself. She was the first woman of his experience who almost persuaded him to believe that her sex might some time prove capable of being both reasonable and reasoning. There was, first, the infinite courtesy and generosity of her heart. She not only showed affection for his second wife's children, she even restored his first wife's portrait to an honorable position on his drawing-room wall. Felicity honestly admired and diligently cared for Lydia's possessions—her Sheraton tables, her Irish silver, and her Lowestoft bowls.

She no less quietly defended Miranda's memory, and besought compassion for her and her children and their miserable death. Such gallantry toward her predecessors was startling enough in its indications of a truly liberal mind, but when in addition Tracy found himself often reading aloud to her in the evening, sometimes even from those "infidel" books, and that her comments on them were neither prejudiced nor dull, he began to wonder if he had not misjudged female sagacity.

But this idyllic autumnal companionship lasted only a short time. And even across those few short years another war cast its somber shadow. In April 1813 the sails of English ships once more reappeared on the Sound, and those old people who, like Tracy, could remember the same sight thirty years before watched them with foreboding and dread. All the old bitterness about the previous destruction of 1781 was revived—particularly the savagely merciless treatment of the few Americans by the overwhelming English in old Fort Griswold on the Groton side of the river.

Nor had they forgotten the hateful figure of Benedict Arnold. They could still recite those verses—said to have been written by Arnold's cousin—which were an acrostic on the traitor's name:

> Born for a curse to virtue and mankind,
> Earth's broadest realm ne'er knew so black a mind.
> Night's sable veil your crimes can never hide,
> Each one so great, 'twould glut historic tide.
> Defunct, your cursed memory will live,
> In all the glare that infamy can give.
> Curses of ages will attend your name,
> Traitors alone will glory in your shame.

Almighty vengeance sternly waits to roll
Rivers of sulphur on your treacherous soul—
Nature looks shuddering back, with conscious dread,
On such a tarnished blot as she has made.
Let hell receive you, riveted in chains,
Doomed to the hottest focus of its flames!

Even the assurances of the British Commander, Sir Thomas Hardy, failed to quiet them, though he seemed exceedingly polite and humane for a foe. His landing parties paid for what they took, he gave his prisoners decent treatment, he kept his promises not to disturb the fishermen, and otherwise behaved in a very chivalrous manner.

But on the first of June two American frigates and a sloop-of-war were driven into New London Harbor, and the port was blockaded. From that time until the end of the war in 1815 there was constant excitement in the town, with continuous petty warfare all along the coast, although the enemy did not attempt to follow the three American ships up the river. And the city of New London was not entered or bombarded, in spite of almost daily predictions that it would be.

So many rumors, with their continuous reminders of the past, at length preyed upon Tracy's mind. Early one morning Felicity found him under the old apple tree in the garden. In a hole he had dug there he was again burying the big green Chinese jar. She called to him, but when he looked up at her it was without recognition. And he only gazed with additional bewilderment into the faces of his children when they came running out of the house. Even the house itself, after Felicity had finally persuaded him to go in, seemed one that was strange to him. He stood first in one room and then in another, shivering wretchedly, yet when she started to light a fire for him on the hearth, he cried out at the sight of the flames in so agonized a voice that she led him away upstairs and got him back into his bed. Outside in the garden the jar lay buried for many weeks before she dared to speak of it, or to have it taken up again.

Sometimes after that day the old man recovered himself, and went about his affairs in a rational way. But much of the time he was childlike, piteously dependent upon Felicity's strength and gentleness, and her calm voice relating to him the cheerier incidents of his own life, recalling old happy times and friends, bringing him back to the present and trying, as quietly as possible, to keep him there unperturbed.

The children continued to confuse him, though now more than anyone else he liked to have them near him. Once, holding Turner on his knee, he called the wondering little boy Christopher, saying that this time the boy had come home safely with no blood on him.

But he was happiest of all after he discovered his flute, laid away so long ago at the back of a drawer in a cupboard upstairs. Neither his lips nor his lungs were what they had been once, but notwithstanding, the faulty, quavering airs enchanted the children who sat on three small stools at his feet while he bent his head to play for them, his fingers fumbling and his foot tapping the floor. The small boy Turner watched that foot in fascination. On it was a buckle of glistening white stones set into wrought silver. The buckle twinkled as the foot tapped, so that tiny friendly eyes seemed to wink and sparkle, as if the music had started some delicious kind of fairy joking especially for him. Tracy himself watched the buckle too. Or perhaps it was the still handsome contour of his leg in its silk stocking that he regarded with so admiring an eye, for he still wore the old-style short breeches, scorning the new French fashion.

There the old man sat in his big armchair, with the children around him, on that winter day when Felicity came to tell him that the news of peace had arrived. He looked up at her and nodded, and smiled as if he understood her well enough but it didn't really matter so much after all. She stood in the doorway watching them for a while—the contented old gentleman playing his flute so badly, Joshua leaning on the arm of the chair scowlingly intent, Abigail at his feet, pursing her lips as her fat fingers worked away on her sampler. But it was mostly Turner who made her smile. The buckle had commenced to gleam again, and its lively sparkle was reflected in his whole delighted little face.

CHAPTER IX

MY DEAR SON

A FEW years after Tracy's death Felicity moved back to Norwich Town. With the help of an older brother who had not followed his father to New York, and also of some of the Leffingwell kin, she found a pleasant house at the lower end of River Road beneath Sentry Hill. There she established herself with the three children, Abigail, Joshua, and Turner, and all the possessions of her own and Tracy's, for which she had an almost religious sentiment.

Tracy did not leave them penniless, and Felicity could always receive additional help from her relatives—when she was not too proud to ask it. Nevertheless she found herself in that difficult position once described as being "in straitened circumstances." Yet she left no record, either on paper or in the memories of her household, of ever once acknowledging fear, helplessness, self-pity, or resentment. Quite calmly she set to work planning and contriving, her head still high, her figure as straight as a soldier's.

The first break in the family came when, somewhat surprisingly, dumpy, demure little Abigail married a well-to-do merchant down at the Landing—a Mr. Z. Pollock Spooner. He was a great deal older than she and at first they seemed ill-matched, but Abigail, to whom girlhood had never been becoming, assumed a handsome middle-agedness almost immediately. In time they became quite a force in the life of the town, for Mr. Spooner's house was large, his business profitable, and his nature moral and charitable. Although they were always "a childless couple," the phrase as applied to them never seemed to suggest disappointment or inadequacy, but merely to add to their air of respectability and worth. Shortly after his sister's marriage Joshua, for whom Mr. Spooner provided work in his office on the wharf, also went to live in the Spooner home.

Left by themselves, Felicity and Turner contrived happily enough. But Felicity was ambitious for her son. Particularly she wanted him to have schooling, and eventually the best preparation available in or near the town for the profession of law. For of course he was to be a lawyer like his father. It never occurred to either of them to plan for anything else.

The little boy's first experience with a schoolmaster on the Green was a very pleasant one. An indolent, snuff-taking man, Mr. Rufus Simpson used to nod and drowse quite often at his desk. He called his ruler "Old Goldings," and sometimes told the boys they could go out and play if they would first step up and take two licks from Old Goldings. Whenever he saw a hand extended, he never had the heart to strike more than once—a cheap price, the boys thought, to pay for escape from school. At other even gayer times, Mr. Simpson declared holiday for all the children. He would take them fishing, or try out a new gun for their amusement in the field behind the schoolhouse.

But after a while the disapproving parents replaced the carefree Mr. Simpson with another and far stricter master. And it was not only on weekdays that this Mr. Goodwill Bliss maintained his intimidating attitude toward the young. One Sunday forenoon Turner met him on a hill-side pasture and excitedly asked him whether he had seen a swarm of bees that he and some other boys had found the day before. Mr. Bliss stood there amid the rocks of the pasture and said severely:

"Young man, aren't you ashamed to speak to me of bees on Sunday morning?" Poor little Turner took to his heels and ran home. He was not accustomed to such stern treatment on the Sabbath or any other day.

Felicity was an indulgent mother. Nevertheless she did not attempt to conceal from Turner the fact that he was the son of a poor widow and must work for what he wanted. Turner's nature was not naturally parsimonious, and he did not relish having less than others. He made up his mind that he would get on in the world and some day have and do all that he wanted.

Meanwhile he was industrious and helped Felicity in every way that he could. When he was about fifteen or sixteen, he worked in Mr. Tuttle's store for the salary of fifty dollars a year. Across the Green was another shop kept by Elisha Jones, where the clerk, Frank Manwaring, was a boy about Turner's age. When Turner learned that Frank received seventy-five dollars a year for his services, he lost no time in mentioning the matter to Mr. Tuttle. The old man looked at him for some time in silence, stroking his chin with a bony thumb and forefinger and squinting through his spectacles at this Hoyt boy from New London who seemed to know his own mind and spoke up to him so briskly and yet respectfully.

"We-el," he said at last reluctantly, "if 'Lisha can afford to pay Frank seventy-five, I guess I can afford to pay you the same."

When Turner went home that night and told his mother, they were so excited that they sat up for hours after their usual bedtime, discussing this great advance in their fortunes.

A few years later Turner went to Colchester to study in the Bacon Academy there. Although this was but fourteen miles from home, he felt important and happy, for he had not been separated from his mother before. Now he was to board in a Mrs. Lowman's house, having for roommate a boy named Harrison Hoyt, a second cousin who had come East all the way from Ohio to go to school in Colchester.

Felicity did not arrange this departure for her son without some sacrifice to herself. In order to pay his expenses she took boarders or, as she sometimes wrote to Turner, "made additions to the household." The minister and his wife, a single young man who was a clerk, and the wife and daughter of a ship's captain who had sailed to South America were the first to share Felicity's home. She never reminded Turner that for his sake she had made this difficult change in her private life. If her letters mentioned it at all, it would be in a matter-of-fact and optimistic manner.

My dear Son,

It has been my wishes and intention to have written you for a week past—the recent addition to my family has so increased my domestick cares that I have but little leisure to devote to my Pen—and I fear a great want of amusement to offer you—our town as usual dull. . . . I am much pleased with the addition to my family—have no reason to regret taking them. I find it a helpout and such an one as will render me aid to you through another term—but this we will keep to ourselves.

Then she would immediately set aside her own concerns to plunge into his, giving him either news of his friends at home or affectionate admonitions as to his studies or his health.

I feel great anxiety about your eyes—I would not use them to their injury. I would see if I could not obtain a pair of Glasses that would help you. I think by watching a Pedlar you may find a pair. They might help to keep your eyes where they are.

If she proffered advice, she very cleverly flavored the dose with dashes of personal flattery in order to make it palatable.

> I hope you will be particular to avoid all those who are not perfectly correct in their habits and Ideas—bearing in mind the old maxim Birds of a Feather. . . . You being my only earthly object, I have a great desire to have you a correct and respectable member of the community, well-knowing nature has been bountifull to you in its bestowments of talents of the most estimable if cultivated in the right way. . . . So, my dear Son, be constantly watchful as to your associates—there is so much deceit and art practised in the present day. . . . Youth generally speaking are not sensible what a weight through life a misjudged friendship may be. . . . It is a just saying that to know how to live one life we ought to live Two. . . . I feel that a few words on this subject is sufficient believing your good sense will guide you.

However, when the town afforded her some reprehensible example of waywardness, she lost no time in setting down the dismal details and forwarding them to Colchester. There was, for instance, the case of "your cousin Henry." At one time she wrote that

> he is now laid up with one of his most awfully distressed Turns owing to imprudence—his case is a most deplorable one—the sight of him is truly painfull—his life can be no other than a wretched one—what a picture he is of a youthfull life spent in vicious habits.

It was about this time—the year 1830—that Turner's half-brother Joshua involved himself in serious money difficulties with his brother-in-law Mr. Spooner, and fled to Florida. Several times Felicity had written rather strangely about him. "I can not decide, for the life of me," she said, "whether he would rather be on the wharf or roving." Another time "he seemed to have roused himself from his state of stupour." He came uptown occasionally to call on her, and though apparently there was no ill-will between them, on the other hand neither was there any confidence or sympathy. She once described him as "a holding-back character."

Although Joshua Hoyt was secretive, temperamental, and in the end dishonest, nevertheless Turner had been fond of the older man and mourned his disappearance. Evidently Felicity realized that affection existed between the two, and hoped that Joshua would finally communicate with Turner. "Do you ever hear from your brother?" her letters often asked. But Joshua kept his own counsel. He died in Jacksonville a few years later, but Felicity could never state so untimely an end in so remote a spot with simplicity and certainty. Instead she would say, "He vanished in the swamps of Florida."

In spite of all this drama in Norwich, Felicity's letters often complained that "the town was never duller," or she would commence with some such affectionate apology as this: "I have seated myself to write you, not because I have much news, but feel that I cannot spend a little leisure more pleasantly than in writing to my dear Boy." Yet she always seemed to find an item or two to interest him, even in the quietest weeks. Either a whole family "had sold out and all gone to the Ohio," or some individual "had sailed for Texas to help a relative" who had lost four members of her family in one day during a cholera epidemic. Often, too, there were vague miserable fevers in Norwich. "It is very sickly here," Felicity would write, mentioning that this one "was confined to his bed" or that one "lays at the point of death." Once in a shocked manner she reported that "your benevolent uncle" had been thrown from his horse on a dark night; "wonder was he wasn't killed."

But she did not always dwell on the cheerless. There was a twinkle as she wrote that "Daniel is up here to meeting today—to look at Lucy Lambert there is no doubt." And the same observant eye regarded with great amusement one William Hall. "William is a good deal inclining to be a dandy—he wore a Cloth cap with a large tassell on the top—a Camblet Cloack made in the City style lined and large Tassel hanging in front." Somebody else, too, had a new "cloack," but, she continued loyally, "they neither appeared equal to yours. Joseph Sterry has a new suit of cloaths made from the same piece of Cloth as yours. He tells me he admired your Coat and Pantaloons and would have such a suit." Then she added, somewhat naïvely, "He is one that looks up to you for example—his friendship is worth preserving."

Felicity often showed anxiety about Turner's appearance. Like most proud people with little or nothing to spend on a wardrobe, she was constantly fearful lest one of them should be an object of pity or derision because of shabbiness, particularly to their own neighbors and friends. How she managed to keep herself decently clad she never mentioned. Her whole concern was for him, that he should if possible be elegant, but at the least orderly and immaculate. When he planned to come home for Thanksgiving, she wrote: "When you return, you must remember that you have all your best cloaths with you and not forget them as it will be holydays and you will want to look smart." And in the next letter she admonished him again: "I hope you will continue your great care of all your cloaths, making use of the most inferior ones now, when it is of the leaste importance as dress is not your present object. . . . When at home you know the best must be constantly worn."

Evening after evening when the day's tasks were done, she must have escaped as politely as possible from those "additions to her household" and taken refuge in the small room at the back of the house. There, either she would write to Turner, or she would mend his old pantaloons "to wear with your brown cloth coat," or she would discuss with Polly the best ways of "bleeching" his shirts and a vest.

Polly was part household servant, part Felicity's companion, adviser, and friend, and wholly Turner's adorer. "View me now," wrote Felicity, "seated in the back room at your table writing with Polly setting at my side, the spectacles on trying to read—this picture you have so often seen. I think it will readily strike your recollection. Polly unites with me in much love to you and prayers for your health and blessings." There was seldom a letter from Felicity which did not contain a loving message from Polly, or some mention of her faithful labors or her constant thoughtfulness: "Your sincere friend Polly sends you a great deal of love. A true and sincere friend is she. She is trying to get the milldew out of your white pantaloons."

Felicity showed a curious detachment in regard to religious matters, and in one comment seemed to imply that she was still questioning, still searching. There were frequent revivals in Norwich, and gatherings referred to as "Four-Day Meetings," with services from sunrise to evening. She attended these and reported on them to Turner: ". . . the great revival which had commenced previous to your leaving has taken hold of some of your friends. I will give you a list of them." Here she named ten young men, but "the ladies were too many to enumerate." To her, she said, the "great wonder" was the Presbyterian converts. But she went on to state that "there never was a day equal to the present for religious instruction of every persuasion. I feel it the duty of everyone to seek all the knowledge thay can on this most important subject and fix on some faith."

Her letters contained very few pious injunctions to her son, though she must have realized, even at this early date, that his mind was inclined to be skeptical, not to say irreverent. But if he mentioned the subject, she never neglected to answer him approvingly and reasonably.

My dear Son,

I was glad to hear you had united yourself to a Bible class. I think that will give you great and useful knowledge of the scriptures which you can never obtain other ways. . . . It is my wishes that you should be devoted and very attentive to all religious worship as that will be always a safe and sure guide for you, and without it all here is disorder and confusion.

For the most part she preached him no sermons, but contented herself—if she advised him at all—by emphasizing worldly matters. All through her correspondence are scattered some such sentences as "The good word of the preceptor and your landlady are invaluable. This will be gained by circumspect manners," or "Our money concerns ever keep within your own breast," or "Economy and care must be the order of the day with you and me, then all will come out well."

She reminded him constantly to leave no debts unpaid, and whenever she could she sent him small sums of money. These and her letters, as well as packages of clothing and boxes of food, went over on the stage that passed the house on its way to Colchester. Evidently, after a while the driver, though trustworthy, resented having to deliver so constantly to young Hoyt.

My dear Son,

I received the box with the enclosed Note and should have complied with your request and my promise—that was to fill it immediately and send it again—it was my intentions so to have done—but found the driver so unwilling to take it the first time that I dare not to presume to offer it again. When he see me standing at the door with it he pulled his cap over his eyes, whipped his horses and set off full speed. Polly gave chase and with the help of a man on foot she overtook him . . . he took it . . . gave it a toss on the top of the carriage—I had no Idea that it or its contents would ever reach you.

Sometimes friends or kindly neighbors—a baker or a doctor—would be going in the direction of Colchester. They always told Felicity a day or two ahead so that she would have time to make up a bundle and write a letter. The whole town was sociable and gracious, and every family seemed to be interested in the young people of all the other households.

There were many lively young men in the town, all very busy hoping and planning, scheming and dreaming.

Some of them stopped quite often at Felicity's house on their way to or from the Landing, to chat with her and inquire for Turner. Apparently her well had some medicinal properties, for one youth called occasionally for the special purpose of taking a tumbler of cold water. He was somewhat older than Turner, and Felicity admired him very much, for he had recently passed his law examinations and was about to begin to practice. After one conversation she wrote Turner that this young gentleman had decided to publish one of his orations, commenting shrewdly:

> I fear it will not appear so well in print, as he is naturally a great orator, and so much depends on the manner in a thing of this kind. He has a most wonderful control over his voice and times it to correspond and accord with every sentence—that with his gracefull gestures will be much missed. I think him the handsomest public speaker of a youth I ever heard. . . . I do not call him an easy-mannered man—in any way but that of a public speaker, and there he is strikingly grand. . . . If I am not mistaken you named a Book you had met with—instructing on Oratory. I should think you might improve yourself in reading that.

This book was *The Forum Orator, or, The American Public Speaker*. Turner and his cousin Harrison would lock the door of their boardinghouse room, close the windows, and put their heads together over this earnest advisory volume for embryo orators. They did not want to risk being overheard in their endeavors by passers-by, particularly two young girls who hung around the house only to giggle and run away when the two young men appeared. Without posing before a mirror it was difficult for the students to follow some of the book's directions, such as those in "The Face, Hints Respecting Its Management; Of Lifting Up the Eyes or Casting Them Down; Eyebrows, How They Should Be Managed; The Lips, Not to Bite Them." In addition they must remember which tones of voice to use for Exordium, Narration, Confirmation, Confutation, and Peroration. Though they must not bellow, neither must they mumble—and of course, under no circumstances spit or hem. Then they must control their hands, seldom or never lifting them above the eyes, learning when to place the right hand on the breast, if left-handed, how to arrange.

So complicated a study needed the aid of at least one sympathetic auditor. Harrison and Turner practiced on each other, reading the speeches at the back of the volume, and though at times even their best efforts resulted only in fits of laughter, they persisted. Beneath the ridiculous grimacing and the awkward gestures lay a deadly seriousness of purpose. Both boys spent much time in speculating on their futures, seeing them always at the least exciting, and sometimes daring to predict that they would be spectacular. Felicity's modest desire that her son should "become a respectable member of the community" faded away entirely in the splendor of Turner's dreams for himself.

Many a less confident and eager boy might have shrunk away from so great a burden as he bore—not only of his own visions but of the hopes of others. But not Turner Hoyt. When his mother wrote that his uncle had spoken "handsomely" of him and viewed him as "a youth of great promise," Turner emphatically agreed with his uncle. If again she happened to remark, "Your relatives all seem to be making great calculation on you, and I have the natural vanity to think they will not be disappointed," his own natural vanity calmly accorded with hers.

During that year at the Bacon Academy only one experience undermined in the least Turner's belief in himself and his own powers. To his astonishment, and later to his humiliation, he discovered that Felicity was not the only kind of woman who could strongly influence him and establish herself in his thoughts—even against his will—past all forgetting. Unlike the other two Colchester misses who loitered near his house only to run at his approach, there was another bolder girl, Katharine Hawthorne, who followed him not only on the street but even up to his room if she knew that Harrison had left the house and the landlady, Mrs. Lowman, could be eluded.

The girl would poke inquisitively into his cupboards and bureau drawers or, using his comb, preen herself before his mirror, patting her brown ringlets into place. She had a sidelong way of glancing at him out of half-closed eyes, her lips curved in a sly smile. Turner did not like her snaky ways at first. She embarrassed him and made him feel awkward and unknowing. She seemed to be expecting something from him, waiting for him to accept the challenge—if it was a challenge—that lay behind the drowsy mockery of her small white face. Once she asked him if he had ever touched a woman. To hide his bewilderment he merely smiled scornfully as he bustled about the room pretending to rearrange his books and papers. He tried to ignore her, to forget her, most of all not to admit that he feared her. But he began to watch for her to saunter past the house, to be cruelly disappointed if she failed to come, and in the end he sought her out sometimes himself.

Turner neglected many things for Kate's sake, and then would wonder why he had. Weeks would pass before he remembered to write Felicity. When a letter came from her, he would read it in a mood that was half petulance and half remorse. But the remorse usually won, and the petulance mounted into something almost like sullen hatred, transferred to Kate and all her troublemaking kind. He had work to do, a way to make, worlds to conquer. Meanwhile he had a patient, courageous, and aging mother who thought of him with such unwavering love and confidence as her "only earthly object." Turner would then sit down and write to her at once, and the last moment at night, before he turned to sleep, he would reread some of Felicity's grave, gracious sentences.

> My dear Son,
>
> . . . do get a long letter written. Every line from you is precious in the eyes of your widowed mother. . . . To hear from you in good health and well-doing is the first wish of my heart. . . . That every blessing may be your attendant is the constant prayer of your affectionate Mother.

After leaving Colchester Turner spent part of the two years 1832-34 at Washington College in Hartford. Although they were filled with new friendships and wider interests, he was restless. For one thing, his poverty still irked him. He could not patiently remain a student when he longed to be fully mature and out in the world. It was high time, he thought, for him to stand in a position where he could give to his mother instead of take from her.

Nevertheless he amused himself, as was evidenced by a journal which he had started the previous summer. He joined a literary society and had the happy experience of seeing a comedy that he had written presented in the college chapel. "The chapel was thronged," announced the journal exuberantly. "Crowds went away for want of room even to stand."

Nor did he neglect his oratory, for about this time he occasionally gave temperance addresses in various near-by small towns. These were a part of his preparation for a political career. Both Turner and his cousin Harrison had decided in the Colchester days that the law was to be only a means of progressing to other and grander honors. Once he mentioned that the highest price paid him for such an address was five dollars, and added plaintively, "I would cheerfully have delivered two today for half the money."

In the fall of one year he had his first chance to look upon a great man, though his journal mentioned the fact with complete placidity:

> The Hon. H. Clay visited the city of Hartford. Four of us were appointed a committee to wait upon him and invite him to visit the college. The next day we escorted him up in a barouche with the Bishop. The students received him with the faculty at the chapel door and he visited the public rooms.

In December of 1833 the offer of a position as teacher lured Turner away from college for four months. He had written his mother of this opportunity, and she had replied, earnestly disapproving:

I do not think you in nature are calculated for a Schoolmaster. You have no idea of the perplexity of a Teacher. I view it as one of the most trying situations you can possibly place yourself. To give the parents satisfaction and peaceably instruct the children is next to impossible. . . . I remember one observation you once made to me about keeping school—that it was a mean way of getting an education. I fully join with you in that opinion—my pride revolts against it. . . . But still, my dear Son, I never mean to oppose your wishes. I expect to yield to them, hoping and praying that all will be well.

Nevertheless Turner could not resist the temptation to test himself in a responsible post. He was not much over twenty at the time and some of his scholars could have been only a little younger, but he recorded his four months with them in a very airy, superior manner:

Dec. 9, 1833—Left college this day to take the principalship of the Academy at Winsted, a Society in the town of Winchester—Litchfield County. I roomed with a young Lawyer and ate at the Public House. Found teaching The Young Idea rather a delightful task. Had at most 38 scholars, Male and Female. Enjoyed myself very much. Found the inhabitants rather a jolly set. A Lyceum was established which met weekly and contributed much to my amusement. Held forth in it every evening. Gave them one short Temp. Address.

The following August he left college, whether through impatience, lack of interest, or lack of funds he did not say, but merely noted, "I took my English diploma and quit." That autumn marked the beginning of his law studies in the office of Jedediah Avery. Jed Avery was the young orator so much admired by Felicity in the Colchester days. He was just enough older than Turner, and successful enough to impress the younger man and to be considered by him as an excellent model for both intellect and deportment.

From his flute-playing father Turner inherited at least some curiosity about music. He belonged to a Mozart society, and he went to the "singing-school" connected with the choir of the meetinghouse. Most of the dances were given informally in the homes, both young and old attending. Turner's journal made note of one affair, held on a fall evening, which began in the parlor but ended in the kitchen, where there was more space and a clearer floor. A novelty was provided by "young Mrs. Huntington and a Spanish gentleman who waltzed," but the evening ended in homely New England style with "old Doct. Perkins taking a heel and toe rather by himself with hat and cane in hand."

But people, amusements, and even the study of law are often crowded out in the journal to make space for the reports of political conventions and town meetings. Turner began to emerge a little from the crowd, acting twice as delegate, the second time in New Haven, where his hundred and twenty-six associates appeared to him "a very respectable and talented body of men." Another year he "was made an Elector at the City Hall." But in March 1835, at a meeting of the Young Whigs he really let himself loose in a long speech, evidently for the first time. By then he had forgotten such juvenile aids as books on oratory. Instead he concentrated fiercely on his subject of the moment, which happened to be a bitter criticism of the Jackson administration. Some of the sentences in this speech must have resounded dramatically enough, with or without the proper accompanying gestures.

The eyes of the people are open to the truth. They see that Andrew Jackson has openly and wantonly violated those promises he made upon entering into office—that his many pledges to the people are unredeemed, and that all his splendid plans of suddenly enriching the people have never been effected, or, if attempted, have failed in the attempt. They were told that economy was to be the order of the day, but our national expenditures have been increased millions annually. They were told that retrenchment was to be one of the leading measures of the administration—but instead of decreasing the executive patronage, it has been increased to such an extent that it looks as if the executive intended to overawe the people by an army of office-holders. The task of reform, too, was to be accomplished, and the Augean stable cleansed. It has been a reformation! A reforming *out* of able, faithful officers, and a reforming *in* of such creatures as B——— and K——— and E———, men who are the very personification of incompetency, corruption and depravity. . . . The Tory party claims to be the old Republican party, and appeals to the democracy of the country. Democracy! Sir, is the magical word that binds its thousands to the Jackson car. Democracy is the mantle that is used to conceal the hideous features and frightful form and cloven foot of Jacksonism.

The rest was a eulogy of his own candidates, and a prophecy that the Jackson party would fall—"like Lucifer never to rise again." He ended on the ardent hope that "old Connecticut, the land of steady habits, will be the last state to prove recreant to the Republican cause."

Alas for his hopes and his prophecies! On April 6 he admitted dismally that the state had "gone all hollow for Jackson." He himself, poor, excitable Young Whig, collapsed under the strain of such heroic efforts and the subsequent disappointment. The next statement in the journal was a rueful one: "Have been sick for some ten days past, but by the virtue of salts, oil, calomel, paragoric and antimony, have finally got up on my legs again."

He solaced himself by buying a round table and a stand-up desk for his room. And he found relief in Jed Avery's office, where he applied himself with renewed vigor to his *Blackstone,* his *Swift's Digest, Stephen on Pleading, Kent's Commentaries,* and other books. For lighter reading he made a vow to go through all of the New Testament, though fortunately not within a specified time, for he found it all too easy in his spare hours to bury himself in the pages of some novel. Several Sundays he put off churchgoing until the afternoon in order to indulge in such works as *Maxwell* or *Cyril Thornton* or *Waverley*. Some of this reading occasionally influenced the style of his journal in a startling manner. All his natural gaiety and delight in being alive would vanish completely behind some assumed attitude of cynical disillusionment. "This world," he announced once, "is cold, heartless, selfish and unprincipled, and one must be cold, selfish, if not unprincipled to succeed in it."

Also, after what must have been a persistent and determined search on his part, he discovered one whom he felt worthy of a vindictive passion—an enemy, "a man whom I hate above all other men. . . . He has injured me, and added insult to injury. Time may give me an opportunity to revenge myself. . . . *'I bide my Time.'* I may reach him yet. I am not generally thwarted in my purposes."

Fortunately he forgot to strut, glower, and mutter in this fashion more often than he remembered. He would be off to call on Mrs. Trumbull, an entertaining old lady of eighty, "a living record of men and manners when she was young." After spending a delightful hour with her he would go home with books from her library under his arm—numbers of the *Spectator,* or *The History of Jacobinism,* or some volume recommended to him by his "esteemed old friend." Or he bustled around as a marshal at an event very important to the town and state, as he solemnly noted.

> Nov. 18 1835—This day will long be remembered by the present citizens of Norwich. The occasion of breaking ground for the Norwich and Worcester Railroad was no ordinary one. It is presumed that nearly ten thousand persons were present. The ground was broken by his Hon. the Governor, and speeches were made. . . . One thousand ladies were under the tent.

Felicity's finances seem to have taken a turn somewhat for the better in these days. Instead of boarders her house often filled up with visitors—friends or relatives. But she enjoyed people, and somehow their presence did not seem to interfere with Turner's studies or occupations. He began now to want lawbooks of his own, and in order to raise money to buy them he tried his hand at various kinds of writing for publication—romantic tales with such titles as "The Monastic Banditti" and "The Reformed Gangster," or political pieces like a "Satire on Emigration," or essays on "pedagogueing" which he sometimes called "Pages from a Student's Diary," and sometimes simply "Reminiscences." His mind went off at queer tangents and sought in odd places for material when he found his own experience or imagination lacking. One Sunday afternoon he amused himself "preparing an article on the ancient institution of the Illuminati, a secret infidel society that flourished in Germany."

Connecticut apparently abounded in publications with such elegant names as *The Pearl* and *The Amaranth,* and there were always, of course, newspapers in the near-by towns as well as those at home in Norwich. Sometimes, too, the *Anti-Masonic Intelligencer* and the *New England Magazine* accepted his efforts, though in the end he had the best luck with the *New Yorker,* which paid him promptly, as he always recorded: "Received this day a communication from H. Greely, Editor New Yorker, enclosing five dollars for two extracts from my Students Diary."

And all through the pages of Turner's journal, from 1832, when he began it, until its end in 1836, flitted the figure of the elusive, provocative Katharine Hawthorne. He would mention going to Colchester with her in the stage, or meeting her at a party when she visited in Norwich. Between such glimpses they corresponded, and he always made a note of each letter that he sent. His moods toward her changed with bewildering swiftness. If he sent her a lock of hair in September, by November he would say carelessly: "Penned an epistle to Kate. Short but friendly. She was pretty but is now growing old and faded. So goes the world." Finally she wrote him that she thought of marrying, to which he replied, "advising her by all means to do it."

But Turner could not quite believe that Kate meant what she said. After some months had passed and she still remained unwed, he went to Colchester to investigate, with the excuse that he wanted to buy some books from an acquaintance there. He found another young man named Bishop "hanging around Kate trying to be intimate with her. He looked rather dissipated and broken down." Feverish with jealousy, he saw even the man whose books were for sale through a distorting mist, describing him as "in a miserable state of health; his appearance indicated approaching dissolution." In fact the whole day was an agonizing experience, and his last comment upon it revealed a very distraught young law student indeed: "I am of the opinion that Bishop intends to seduce Kate if he can."

That was in July. On August 27 he went on a sailing expedition to Gardiner's Island with his uncle. It was evidently a birthday treat, but he barely mentioned it before rushing into some very gloomy thoughts inspired to some extent by this personal anniversary, but mostly by the disastrous news from Kate:

> Twenty-five years old today—And where shall I be one year from now? What changes will take place during that period in my own views, circumstances, character, in my circle of friends and kindred? No one can foretell. Dark and uncertain indeed is the future. One year from today and perhaps the heart I now feel beating will have ceased its pulsations forever, and the hand which now guides this pen may have mouldered into dust. Kate Hawthorne is to be married to G. W. Bishop. And why need that trouble me? What is her fate to me? I have felt low-spirited ever since I heard of it.

His melancholy continued until two days afterward, which was the day of Kate's wedding. He could not trust himself to be present at this ceremony. Instead he stayed at home and tried to ease the unbearable burden on his heart by "committing to the pages of my Diary the secret of my acquaintance with Katharine Hawthorne."

The way in which he scented and beribboned this simple, rather sordid first love affair of his was astonishing. Nevertheless here and there, in spite of posturings and pretenses, an occasional cry of honest hurt burst harshly through. When he writes, "There was a witchery about her I could not resist," or "At times I wish I had never known her," the ludicrous pose fades away, and there alone in his room on a summer evening stoops the young man over his stand-up desk. He has laid down his pen for a moment—"My arm is now wearied and my heart is sick"—and has covered his face with his hands. But for the most part his painful little tale is cloaked, and very darkly cloaked, in a heavy style:

> One hour ago and Kate was undoubtedly united for life to that low, unprincipled brute of a Bishop—The night is dark and gloomy enough—perhaps an augury for them! I had anticipated being present—perhaps it was well I did not go. Bishop might have been jealous of *me* and abused *her*.
>
> Katharine Hawthorne is the second child of Richard Hawthorne and Amelia Brooks. They came originally from Wethersfield. Kate used at times to tell me that she owned land there, inherited from her mother. I never could learn of any except the spot occupied by her in the churchyard. . . . Her mother died when Kate was young, and being brought up in a public house, she met with company from every section of the states. Pretty, interesting in her manner, and possessed of consummate address, she soon won attention. Too much of it rendered her fickle, heartless and coquettish. . . . She certainly was not distinguished for her intellectual superiority. Neither had fashionable life moulded her manners. Perhaps her influence over me may be ascribed to my own inexperience. . . . Previous to this

my knowledge of women had been limited to narrow bounds—the society of chaste females. . . . I was but a *boy* when I first knew her—in one year I became *old* in vice, experienced in the arts of dissimulation, corrupt at heart, and ever ready to conceal crime by falsehood. How easy is the transition from virtue to vice!

Perhaps so severe an indictment of Kate, once it was down on paper, staggered even Turner himself, for at this point in his story he broke off, saying he would finish "this sketch" on the following day. He could not have spent an entirely sleepless or uncomfortable night, for when he again resumed his reminiscences he had somewhat softened his judgment. He even went so far as to reassure himself somewhat:

She was always true to me, and I sincerely believe loved me. Fanny Hart of Colchester also loved me, but I could attend to but one at a time. . . . Kate never loved Bishop, and has married him I have no doubt rather than live an old maid.

But it was in this grandiose attempt to disguise himself as the triumphant villain of the piece that he most fully revealed the actual quality of their wretched warfare.

By various arts she tried to make me offer to marry her. Many a time she put up individuals to advise me to do it. But I had gained a little too much knowledge of the world. I proved too apt a scholar for my instructress. I in time turned the tables upon her. I made her come under my yoke as I had long borne hers. She soon yielded in all things to me except one.

But he did not really deceive himself. Better than anyone he knew that Kate, the hatefully desirable, the never-possessed, had outwitted and defeated him. There she would stand forever in his memory looking at him over her shoulder with her tantalizing, enigmatic smile. He might moralize as much as he chose by saying, "I gained an admirable knowledge of human nature from my acquaintance with her," but that such reflections only added to his bitterness he admitted when he added that it was a "knowledge bought at the expense of good principles. 'I have paid dear for the whistle.'"

The following week, at somebody else's wedding, he encountered Kate for the last recorded time. No doubt he had hoped to find her the very picture of an abused, woebegone, and regretful bride. He had to concede grudgingly that "she seemed in tolerable spirits."

After this account of Katharine Hawthorne there were only a few pages remaining in the journal, and they were devoted to the conscientious mention of some "delightful parties" as well as reports of his final preparations for his examinations. He was very much in earnest about this whole matter and expressed himself quite solemnly: "Thurs. Nov. 10—Today I took the oaths required on being admitted an Attorney and Counsellor at Law. My application was handed in to the bar meeting yesterday noon. No objection was made."

In the evening he was examined by a formidable array of questioners, including not only lawyers from Norwich but judges from Lyme and New London. It all passed off successfully, and he commented soberly: "A new career is now open to me. Everything depends upon my own exertions."

Over Sunday he relaxed by reading *The Merchant of Venice,* and Monday morning he left for four days in New York for a holiday, and to buy the rest of his law library before opening his own office. If on the way to the city he devoted any time to thoughts about himself and his future, no doubt they were cheerful ones. Perhaps he remembered and repeated that first, least lugubrious, and most genuine of all his statements written down on his previous birthday:

"Today I am twenty-five. The second important period in a man's life has come. It is the *finest.*"

CHAPTER X

ELIZABETH: THE ENGLISH WIFE

SO IN the end Felicity realized her dream for her son. She saw him a lawyer as his father had been before him, a young man who in spite of his high spirits and his love of fun was very serious about his life and his work, and very ambitious. He prospered, and Felicity, who felt the end of her own life approaching, began to look about her for a suitable wife for this adored only son. But no one in the town seemed to her worthy. Turner may have surmised that her approval would be difficult to win, so when at last he made his choice, it was away from home, and the whole affair was maneuvered with such decisiveness and speed that his startled mother saw no course left open to her except a calm acceptance.

In the year 1841 Turner went to New York in connection with some work on one of his cases. There he met Mrs. Elizabeth Dodd Harris, a young Englishwoman and a widow. When he went to the city a second time not long after, they became engaged, and on his third trip they were married.

No doubt he felt it to be especially and blessedly right that Elizabeth should be a widow. After all these fatherless years with Felicity, naturally a widow would appeal to him as a woman he could love with the most nearly complete understanding. And in her Englishness he sought, perhaps unconsciously, for some actual possession of his mother's sentimental musings about England. But Elizabeth had no titled connections to offer. She was a miller's daughter who had followed her two brothers to America and New York. Her first husband was a sea captain and, oddly enough, she had lived in Groton across from New London during the short space of this earlier marriage. She dropped her *h*'s in a way which amused and fascinated Turner but which disconcerted Felicity a good deal. Felicity was charmed, however, by Elizabeth's fair, softly flushed cheeks, the radiance of her smile, and the quiet, unassuming manner with which she endured the necessary introductions and inspections in Connecticut.

But Felicity was old, and perhaps she overemphasized

and tiresomely repeated all those memories so endeared to her by the lost years and the pride so gallantly sustained. One afternoon when for the thousandth time Elizabeth had heard of Tracy Hoyt, his wives, and his wives' possessions, as well as the anecdotes of Felicity's own people, she rebelled.

"Ah, well," she remarked, a trifle wearily, "I'm not a Turner, nor an Adgate, nor a Saltonstall. I'm just plain Elizabeth Dodd from Oxon, England."

She created some excitement in Norwich Town. People said that Turner Hoyt had married a "foreigner," and little girls tiptoed to the garden wall to peek over at Mr. Hoyt's "English wife." But when she caught them at it and came down the path smiling with nosegays for them in her hand, her strangeness somehow vanished and their hearts were won.

Elizabeth loved the garden—the warm sun on her back as she bent over the roots and seeds, the little showers of bright dew that the leaves shook across her face and throat, the feeling of earth crumbling and falling through her bare hands. And she had the secret and magical gardener's touch—"the green thumb" that made all things growing in that earth flower richly and colorfully. It was Elizabeth who set out the lilies-of-the-valley underneath the grape arbor to delight not only her own children but her grandchildren, whom she was never to know but who would be reminded of her by those sprays of tiny white bells springing up under their feet so faithfully year after year. It was she who added the gooseberry and the currant bushes edging the vegetable garden so that she could make her delicious tarts and pies.

At some window in the house Felicity would stand, rigid and disapproving, staring out at that solitary figure bending among her flowers, withdrawn into a world of her own through long, bright afternoons. Nor did she ever share in the ice-cold pitcher of ale that Elizabeth liked to have waiting for her in the darkened pantry when her hours in the sunlight were over. Felicity lived long enough to hold her first grandchild—Philip—in her arms, but when Mary was born nine years later, Felicity had been dead for some time.

Between those two living children Elizabeth, like other women of her time, lost many babies. Even had they survived, it is doubtful if her passionate worship of Philip would have been in any way changed or diminished. He gave her in return a shy devotion never openly expressed, revealing itself only in a constant desire to be near her wherever she might be in the house or the garden. Sometimes, playing beside her, when he thought she was not looking he would reach out a small hand and softly stroke her dress or touch her shoe. She never tired of gazing at him, at his shock of light hair that later darkened ruddily, his deep-set gray eyes, and his full, sweet, sensitive lips. Philip's face, even in childhood, was curiously overcast with a shadow of melancholy that often troubled his mother. And sometimes she was sharply pierced by a brief glimpse into the thorny tangle of his spirit, which his mature reticence so carefully and so tensely strove to guard. But he could make her laugh too, with his odd way of saying droll things while keeping his features perfectly composed, a technique of fun exactly the opposite of his father's, whose method was openly gleeful and hilarious.

Philip and his father never really found the way to one another's hearts. Perhaps it was in the nature of Turner's affections to spend themselves on a daughter rather than a son. And he had a strong possessive streak, a quality particularly resented by a temperament like Philip's. But both the mother and the father realized—one with the heart and the other with the mind—that in this son who could so puzzle and charm them there was a challenge, almost frightening, to their powers of understanding. Infancy seemed to be a state that not only did not attract Turner, but alarmed and somewhat repelled him. Both his children bored him until they were well grown out of babyhood, but then he began to supervise their education and their training with an almost furious eagerness.

Philip went first to a small school on the Norwich Town Green, just up the street and around the corner from home. Mrs. Lathrop and her niece Letitia were the teachers, all that were necessary for their few scholars. The house was small and brown, with a roof that sloped down longer at the rear than in the front and with lilac and syringa bushes clustering close to the windows and around the small, plain doorway. Mrs. Lathrop's devotion to Philip soon almost equaled that of his mother. His mind had not only quickness but a kind of quaintness that delighted and surprised her. For a while arithmetic got the better of him, and one evening at the supper table he said very sadly:

"Father, I don't understand long division, and I never will."

Turner laughed. He himself, never an expert at figures, had been known to remark that if the result he got from adding up the meat bill differed from that of the butcher, he always paid according to the butcher. So he was not seriously perturbed by his child's moment of despair.

Now and then Philip came home proudly bearing a Reward of Merit. This was a paper slip on which was inscribed "For Diligence and Good Behaviour" at the top, with his name at the bottom, the center decorated with a little colored picture of Mary and her lamb, or a portrait of an Indian brave within an oval frame, or tiny cherubic figures bending over musical instruments, or a book and a globe. Or it might have a printed verse:

> Here you will find your teachers are kind,
> And with their help succeeding,
> The older you grow, the more you'll know,
> And soon you'll love your reading.

By the time that Mary, the little sister, went to Mrs. Lathrop's school, Philip was already in the Norwich Free Academy, delving into Latin and Greek and eagerly devouring all kinds of poetry. He even tried his own hand at writing verse, though carefully concealing or destroying all but the most lighthearted efforts.

Every year the boys in the Academy competed in declamation. Often Turner, as one of the judges, delighted to listen to and watch his son and the sons of his friends as with serious young faces and stiff, adolescent gestures they declaimed such pieces as "Regulus to the Roman Senate," or "The Speech of Spartacus to the Gladiators of Capua," or Byron's "Ode to Venice." All this was considered very good practice for boys destined for the law, and of course Turner intended that Philip should be a lawyer.

Sometimes Philip agreed with his father; at other times

he stubbornly rebelled, and wished that his father would leave his future alone and not expect so much either from him or for him. He hardly knew himself what he wanted, only that often he hated Norwich Town, Connecticut, and dreamed fierce, stormy dreams of running away from it to the far ends of the earth where he could be changed into somebody else besides Philip, the son of Turner Hoyt and the grandson of Felicity. Such dreams made him brooding and silent. When moods of this sort closed down on him, he irritated his father. But his mother, more loving and more intuitive, watched him with a troubled heart. Many a night she tiptoed into his room to look at him asleep, his slenderness sprawled out in the four-post bed, his hands relaxed along the coverlet, his closed eyes more shadowy, more cryptic than ever.

Elizabeth's life through those years was a rich and busy one. The neighbors and friends had grown accustomed to "the Englishwoman," and she herself lost some of her feeling of strangeness, except for that inescapable one which any such woman has of being always a foreigner to her husband's people. Turner, in the Assembly in Hartford, wrote her letters full of his widening interests, his new and old friends, advice and questions about herself and the children. When he came home he would bring something to please her—and incidentally himself, too—some delicate china, a Wedgwood bowl, fragile teacups, or a pair of lavender Alcock pitchers with white figures on the sides.

Very often, also, Turner brought home guests, for his hospitality was impulsive and expansive, and he had a way of asking everyone to seek him out in "old Connecticut."

Whenever he wrote a note, he always added at the end, "Should you be near us in old Connecticut, do not fail to come and see us." They seldom failed. This meant that Elizabeth must keep the house in order and the larder full. She had only one old woman to help her, Bridget Bourke, but the general store and meat market were close at hand up on the Green, and in summer they could depend on their own garden and fruit trees. Fresh eggs and butter came to the house twice a week, brought by the sedate and smiling Mr. Josiah Baxter of Blue Blinds, a farm about twelve miles away, when he came to town for his errands. He had known Felicity too, and he always liked to stop for a chat in the kitchen with Elizabeth, and a dry joke with the small Mary who was about the age of one of his own children.

Mary was usually there, for she liked the kitchen, its sounds and smells, the mysterious transformations that took place under the magic of her mother's hand, and the way old Bridget carried on muttered conversations with rising and falling pot lids or the oven door. Given a spoonful of batter in a small bowl, she would sit at the table stirring aimlessly but with a gravely solemn air. Philip, too, could smell cookies baking a mile away, and always ran in sniffing and looking expectant.

When Philip was almost seventeen, his restlessness boiled over into a kind of wildness that worried Elizabeth and angered Turner. A few of the Norwich Town boys began to meet in a little room behind the store on the Green and play cards, and often, to add to the impression that they were grown men, they filched cigars and a bottle of wine from some father's cellar. These gatherings were finally brought to Turner's attention, and one afternoon, in the midst of a session of hilarity, he burst into the room. Boys fled in all directions, scattering cards, tipping over the chairs and glasses, and exploding with laughter, which was not unmixed with gasps of terror, as the Hoyt temper was well known.

Philip leapt through the window, leaving the greater part of the seat of his trousers fluttering from a nail on the sill. Eventually, when he reached home, this gap in his attire added more than a little to his discomfort during the inevitable scene with his father. Usually Philip came off rather well in those scenes, for though he had a spirit equal to Turner's, he had also what the older man generally lacked—self-control—and both of them knew it. But while it was possible on this particular occasion to maintain his dignity as long as he faced his father, as soon as he turned to leave—and he could not back out of the room without being even more ridiculous—the hot tears sprang out onto scarlet cheeks. He hated being laughed at, even silently, and he knew that his father, having completed his tirade, was grinning at the sight he saw.

The result of all this was that Turner sent the boy away to a small school in Massachusetts whose headmaster was an old friend. To Turner the headmaster soon wrote: "Your son is wide awake and fond of sport. He has good impulses and is reasonably studious, but means to have a good time." Both Turner and Elizabeth, however, felt less anxious about their son than when he had been at home, and the following fall when he entered Union College, they felt that he was grown up and could be trusted. Their hopes for him were high.

But the winter of 1860-61 brought no peace to high-spirited American boys. Already early in the year many of them were leaving the little college in Schenectady, some to go South to their troubled homes, others to households no less troubled in the North. All of them were full of thoughts and feelings about the impending war, and all were eager to fight.

Turner, seeing both the condition of his country and the state of his boy's mind, determined to forestall any foolish move on Philip's part if he could. He offered the boy a trip to Europe on a sailing ship, which he knew meant at least six weeks going over and an equally long return. Probably by the time Philip got back the war would be over. It was a simple matter for Turner to arrange this trip, as he knew the master of just such a vessel, a Captain Bosworth from Lyme. Mrs. Bosworth and her little daughter were always aboard too, which was reassuring to Elizabeth. Philip could not resist this temptation. In the prospect of such a voyage and the chance to see something of the world, he momentarily forgot how much he wanted to be a soldier. Toward the end of March, very happy and excited, he sailed out of New York Harbor on the ship *Elwood Walter,* bound for Antwerp with a cargo of rosin, cotton, flour, coffee, tobacco, and rice, and also a barrel of choice potatoes for King Leopold.

He was still in the same bouyant mood when he wrote his first letter home, headed "At Sea" and giving the exact latitude and longitude in a very seamanlike manner. He had been seasick but had recovered, he had experienced some very dramatic weather, he was eating heartily and the food was good, he walked the quarter-deck at night with the Scotch mate, when they discussed the respective merits of Robert Burns and Walter Scott, and they borrowed one another's books. Elizabeth and Turner drew a long breath, and for a space their anxiety relaxed.

Then came a letter from Antwerp, which said:

> The Captain was ashore this morning, and came on board telling of the *great fight* at Fort Sumter. Everything is as dead as Dorus here on account of the miserable quarrel in the states, and we can not get a single thing in the way of freight to carry back. Perhaps we will go to London or Cardiff, and carry home a load of coals.

Weeks later he wrote from England: "I wish to God I was home to enlist with the other boys. I curse myself every day for being out here not knowing when I shall get back." Turner and Elizabeth said little to one another about that letter, but it restored once more, in both their hearts, the same foreboding and fear.

It was a long voyage back to the States, and the novelty of the days and nights at sea, so full of interest to Philip on the way over, now seemed drearily and monotonously endless. He forgot his books and his desire to study navigation. There was only his hope that they might encounter a privateer and so give him a chance to fulfill his feverish desire to be somehow in the fight.

He was never long out of his mother's mind. No matter through what a wind-swept and dangerous ocean sailed the ship bearing him so slowly home to her, she could only picture it now as a region of safety compared to the battlefields on which his heart was set. Quietly she went about her tasks, talking with the mothers of other boys either gone to the war or on their way. She listened to the tense discussions by Turner and his friends. And she read the newspapers, striving to understand what now indeed had become a foreign language.

Sundays, when the bell tolled in the white steeple of the meetinghouse up on the Green, she took Mary by the hand and together they went up the white road in the dazzling early summer sunshine. The little girl stepped out bravely beside her mother, her small hoop skirt swaying above the white pantalettes and twinkling shoes. Elizabeth began to notice how close the young head came to her shoulder. Philip was small and slender like his father, and Elizabeth herself was short. But Mary, she saw, would be tall like Felicity, and already—almost like a miniature Lady Hoyt—she carried herself with that same patrician elegance and pride, an air which sat very quaintly on her small, bonneted head.

Mary was very fastidious about her clothes, and femininely fond of pretty possessions. Someone had given her a gold bracelet engraved with a design in black. She was always conscious of it on her wrist, lifting and turning her hand, gazing at it with self-satisfaction, her head on one side. Sometimes her love of finery led her astray. One Sunday morning her mother, preceding her as usual up the aisle, heard faint, stifled sounds from the benches already full of worshipers. Glancing over her shoulder, she saw Mary following sedately enough, but with her little ruffled parasol borne, still wide-open, over her head.

All waited for Philip that summer except the season itself. The currants ripened into jeweled clusters on the long line of bushes, the white roses opened and scattered over the green grass. Dust gathered gray in the wrinkled leaves of the nettles that sprang up at the corner of the wall. Beyond in the old burying-ground, the gold-and-white daisies dotted the long grass around the carved stones. Elizabeth, on her knees in her garden, heard the farmer shouting to his horses as he cut the hay in the meadow by the river across the road. She smiled, and said to herself:

"That means rain. It always rains when Burrill mows his field."

Late that night she wakened, and lay in the still, fiery darkness, tensely listening. Then she heard again the sound which evidently had roused her. From far across the river, beyond Wawecus Hill, the low, ugly rumble of thunder pounded faintly. She thought of Philip, and her heart seemed to stop. Fearful lest her trembling should waken Turner, breathing so quietly there beside her, she drew herself over to the edge of the bed and buried her face in the hot pillow. Even then she could not help hearing that sound like heavy guns, coming closer and closer through the breathless, lonely night.

CHAPTER XI

A SOLDIER OF THE CIVIL WAR

EARLY in the fall Philip Hoyt was in Hartford with other Connecticut Volunteers. Elizabeth watched him leave with as much courage as she could summon, but her heart was heavy. Turner, however, faced the inevitable with at least a pretense of cheerfulness.

"Now see here, Philip," he remarked to his son on the day of his departure, "don't you go and get a load of duck-shot in your stern from any damned Georgia trooper!"

The boy realized the extent of Elizabeth's capacity for anxiety about him, and so his first letter was to her.

> You must not worry and fret about me, my dear Mother, as I am in excellent health—never had a better appetite in my life. Why, I believe that after we got through drilling this morning, I was so hungry I could have clawed the letters off a gravestone.

It was a relief to her, too, to read that he had made a call on the regimental doctor—Dr. Robinson from Norwich. She could not imagine that familiar figure rigged out as a soldier, but Philip said that he looked very well in his uniform. And she was thankful that the child had warm blankets and slept like a log.

The regiment moved on to Long Island, where Philip's Uncle Rob, Elizabeth's brother in New York, went out to see him and sent home good reports. He told of a young puppy that Philip and the other boys in his tent had bought, and how they planned, when the war was over, to play a game of pitch to see who would take the little dog home to keep.

In November Philip was in Annapolis, now full of troops from Connecticut, Massachusetts, Pennsylvania, and New York. His letters were full of gossip about old friends, whom he met constantly. Even two of the boys in a New York company had once lived in Bean Hill. His colonel, Thomas Howland, was a neighbor, a lawyer about thirty years old who had an office in the same building downtown as Turner. He too wrote every now and then to reassure the Hoyts about their son, and to exchange political views with Turner.

Philip seemed to be still ravenously hungry, and complained that everyone had received boxes of food from home except himself. When this reproach arrived, Elizabeth and Bridget Bourke fairly flew around the kitchen putting together all the good things that he loved the best—Marlborough pies, sponge cake, a boiled ham, and a bottle of grape wine. By some miracle of good luck they arrived unspoiled and unsmashed, and Philip gave a banquet in Colonel Howland's tent. The Colonel went for the victuals with enthusiasm, but toward the wine he showed a slightly patronizing air. It was too sweet, he objected, and he would have preferred a drink with more bite to it, "something that would cut." His young companion slyly noted for Elizabeth's benefit that the Colonel didn't waste any of it. Elizabeth and Turner both chuckled over the homelike picture presented by this letter, and decided that in the next box they would send a bottle of something more suitable for Tom Howland's mature taste. There was no criticism from Philip himself. "If you only knew," he wrote, "how good things from home taste down here."

All through that fall and early winter of 1861 his letters gave somewhat the impression that the entire boyhood and young manhood of Connecticut were on some kind of fantastic lark down in Maryland, with nothing more to write home about than pleas for cakes and cookies, or small possessions left behind, or messages to be delivered to the neighbors.

But there was one side of army life which the impetuous Philip had not foreseen—and that was its boredom. Discomfort and hardship he accepted, and if he complained, he did so for the most part humorously. When he and the other boys with him discovered that the winter nights could be cold even in "the south," they rigged up a stove-pipe in their tent to carry off the smoke from a fire. "This is a decided improvement," commented Philip. Lack of food, too, could be endured, though it seemed as though he never had been so hungry before. But the monotony of his days became insupportable. His discontent grew into peevishness, and he indulged himself in the most insolent criticisms of all his superiors, from the Governor of Connecticut down to his colonel and good friend, Tom Howland. He had been so sure that going to war meant going to war, and that he would be plunged at once into some high and heroic action. When at length he learned that they were to winter in Annapolis, he wrote home a very indignant letter asking his father to use his influence to have him transferred instantly to another company and get him out of "this hole."

Meanwhile Turner in the Assembly probably knew far more about the plans for troops than Philip did. Moreover, he not only wanted to bring his son out of the war alive; he intended also to have him decked with suitable honors. Philip was Turner Hoyt's son. More was to be expected of him than of any other boy in Connecticut, and more must be received for him. But in planning such a combination Turner continuously forgot the one obstacle stiffest of all to surmount—Philip's own nature. Proud, sensitive, reserved, Philip never tried to ingratiate himself for his own ends as his father did. Already Turner had sent him a letter of introduction to General Burnside, but

Philip disdained to use it and when questioned about it by his mother, he replied:

> Tell Father I have not given that letter to General Burnside, as it would not look well for me to go and see him, and as to making his acquaintance, as you wished me to do in your last letter, why, Mother, the idea is absurd—a second Lieutenant going to see a Brigadier General about nothing—If Father will only let me paddle my own canoe I shall get along well enough.

On Thanksgiving Day and Christmas Philip wrote long letters to Elizabeth. They showed no signs of homesickness, but somehow they saddened her. He was so careful to assure her on the first holiday that he and his friends had been able to find something good to eat, and on the second that he had attended service in a church. She herself was only too satisfied to have him remain in Annapolis provided he did not sicken or starve. If she knew how furiously Turner corresponded with Colonel Howland and others in the army, she was wise enough not to mention it to Philip, and it was some time before he realized and resented it. But shortly after Christmas Philip had some exciting news:

> I have been appointed to the Signal Corps—a body consisting of second Lieuts commanded by a Major. It is a very honorable position. I need money as I must have spurs, gauntlet gloves, white gloves, a bugle, and all sorts of little military fixin's.

And a little later he explained further:

> We are stationed on some eminence and with a telescope watch the movements of a flag miles off—sometimes through a very powerful glass, we then have to give the order to our flagmen by numbers only as no words are used at all. It is a sort of deaf and dumb alphabet. . . . The Code is a new one, just

started, as the old military code was made by Mr. Jefferson Davis. The Rebels are entirely unacquainted with the code used by us. The old code was easy but this one is hard.

At last he was busy, active not only physically but mentally too. He found it necessary to study and to practice constantly and diligently. Torches were used by night as well as flags by day, and often after such a drill he lay awake in bed repeating the code to himself. Philip was interested in this new and untried branch of the service, and he saw in it the hope of a quicker advancement for himself and, best of all, the chance of an early departure from Annapolis. In the latter conjecture he was right, as before long he had started for Roanoke Island on the ship *Colonel Satterlee,* which he referred to contemptuously as "a second-hand coffin." But at least he was up and away.

It was on the coast of Virginia, however, that Philip's delight and pride in his new duties suffered a pathetic deflation. Burnside sent for "a young man named Hoyt" to be one of the two signal officers stationed on his own ship. Philip's astonishment at being thus singled out by so high an authority was mingled with rage. He saw now only too clearly how the long, protective arm of his father had at last reached to him and swept him safely out of the center of danger—at least for the moment. He never directly accused Turner of tricking him, but the bitter tone of one letter at this time spoke for itself:

You ask me if I have formed Burnside's acquaintance, whether he is a pleasant man etc. I have never spoken to him except to say "Yes, Sir," one day when he told me to send a message as we were nearing Roanoke. He has something better to think of than to talk about nothing with a 2nd Lieut. He sent for me to come on board of the "Spalding" and I wish his tongue had been palsied when he gave the order. We were out of range of the guns and could just hear without seeing.

After the fight he went ashore and had his first sight of a battlefield, the hideously wounded dying, the monstrous and inhuman dead. He did not spare those at home one detail of this "truly fearful sight." Poor Elizabeth, accustomed to many readings of each one of his letters, put this one away and never looked at it again.

Philip now began to maneuver things somewhat on his own accord. He had made one good friend, his superior officer in the Signal Corps, an older man who called him affectionately the "Little One." Through the aid of this friend he was transferred from one ship to another, and at length to Beaufort. There during the attack and the surrender of near-by Fort Macon he was allowed to show what he could do as a signal officer. He kept his head admirably, and came through with satisfaction to everyone, including a little too much to himself. His anger against his father cooled, and he wrote him an enthusiastic letter.

Unfortunately Turner then made the one mistake that would again alienate his son. He published the letter. Since all the men received home papers, they were soon reading Philip's exceedingly personal account and passing it around with a derision that was anything but good-natured. They would say, "Well, well, so this is Hoyt—the man who took Fort Macon." Philip's heart was broken, and he sent his father one stinging line: "I'm damned if I write you again as long as I'm in the army."

Then commenced for Philip one of the hardest periods that he had yet faced. After so much feverish excitement and his elation at his success, followed by the humiliation of wounded pride, the Signal Corps itself failed him. His friend and senior officer resigned and went home; Philip was stationed at New Bern with different companions and under laxer discipline, with very little to do. And he was ill with that faithful complaint of all soldiers in strange countrysides, diarrhea. He told his mother that he had cured himself of the first attack by eating a peck of clams, and of a later one by the fact that he could not get anything to eat at all for three days. But behind this airy dismissal of discomfort lay bodily weakness, homesickness, and an overpowering sense of failure. In addition, there seemed to be no end to the idleness and dissipation that he saw around him. Frightened and sickened by "temptations," he determined to get out of the army, and impulsively sent in his resignation. He was now as anxious to return home to Connecticut and go to work in his father's law office as he once had been to get away. And anyway, the war was nearly over.

At this point Colonel Howland reappeared and proved once more to be the reliable and loyal friend. He had seen the way things were going with the Signal Corps in New Bern, but he also convinced Philip that it was not the time to leave the army altogether. His intelligent handling of the younger man succeeded, and Philip was persuaded to leave only the Signal Corps and to return to his regiment.

There was also need for Colonel Howland to quiet Turner, who had not known whether to be mortified or relieved by Philip's swift decision. This the Colonel did by writing a straightforward account of the whole matter, with the soothing additions that he intended to promote Philip to a first lieutenancy, that the boy "was studying tactics pretty closely," and that physically he looked better than ever before.

It was true that Philip went to work with a will in order to forget and recover from his recent lazy life. Perhaps, too, part of his studious application to tactics was due to a memory of Annapolis and his earlier experience there, when he had been disgusted to see an officer trying to drill his men with his book hidden under his coat.

In spite of his threat never to write his father again, they were now once more corresponding. But only too soon there were signs that the constant clashing of their personalities had not ceased. Turner published no more of Philip's letters, but he could still not resist trying to direct and domineer. This time, however, his attempts came from a different quarter. If Philip would not lower himself to make friends with a general, possibly the devotion of privates could force him into what Turner considered a valuable popularity. But the unmanageable boy balked at this scheme with the same stiff pride. And now the words were set down by a hand that clearly and decidedly was maturing.

> I am old enough and able to take care of myself without help from any damned Irishman from Mystic. I am tormented to death by a Greek named O'Halloran who claims to be a very intimate friend of yours. I think you miss it by picking up and making so much of such fellows.

But there was never any chafing irritation between Philip and his mother. Whatever tenderness he had he kept for Elizabeth. This had always been true, though even with her in his childhood any tendency toward too much demonstration had been held strictly in control. Remembering this, she hardly knew whether to be happy or miserable when one note to her ended wistfully, "I love you very much and think of you every hour." Surely, she thought, a loneliness almost too heavy to be borne lay behind that pathetic sentence, so astonishing in this reserved boy, who ordinarily never so much as signed himself "Affectionately yours," but only "Your son, Philip Hoyt."

During that summer he came home on a few days' leave. His family had not seen him for almost a year. In his uniform he seemed to them taller and, in some inexplicable way, like a handsome visiting stranger. That melancholy in his eyes, which had always been noticeable but only as an elusive shadow, had deepened, and his whole expression was older and sterner. He took his little sister on his knee as a grown man would have done, teasing her as she looked up at him with shy admiration. But it was a gentler teasing than it had been once. She bore it without resentment, only coloring a bit when he called her "Tige"—his own name for her, first bestowed long ago after a fierce display of temper. But she smiled too as she softly stroked the sleeve of his blue coat.

Philip slept peacefully in his own bed with the four rounded posts. When he was small, he used to stare at those posts as he knelt beside the bed to say his prayers. They looked like heads silently watching him and listening. They became such real presences that they frightened him, until the night he finally asked his mother who they were. Standing beside him, holding the candle, she softly named them for him in a way that transformed them forever after into patient guardians of the dark:

> Matthew, Mark, Luke, John,
> Bless the bed that I lie on.
> Before I lay me down to sleep
> I give my soul to Christ to keep.
> Four corners to my bed,
> Four angels there aspread,
> Two to foot, and two to head.
> If any danger come to me,
> Sweet Jesus Christ, deliver me.

So now, though he scarcely believed it himself, he was returned once more to the safe comfort of Matthew, Mark, Luke, and John. The window of his room at the head of the stairs looked out over the garden and the old burying-ground beyond. Through those few summer nights, while he lay there the breeze drifted in lightly, sweet with the fragrance of the dewy meadow grasses. The long, white moonlight traveled across the wall in a dazzling shaft, just as he had watched it on hundreds of other soundless midnights. Were those other places, those other darknesses, nothing but a weird dream? Who was that old man, haggard with fever and approaching death, that he had come upon in a lonely shack in the midst of a dense pine wood, who had raised himself feebly on his tumbled cot as he cried out hoarsely, "May God Almighty help your Cause!"?

What a long march it had been through those pines, so tall and so thick at the tops that he had grown confused about time and had thought the day was night. Then they had stumbled into the clearing and found the dreary, tumble-down house. And what of those others in an open field who did not speak at all, who had once been men but were now only so much raw meat, laid open like something in a butcher's shop for the flies to crawl over? Was there any meaning in the sound of such syllables as North Carolina and Virginia?

He did not try to answer but, turning over in bed in the familiar room, saw on the moonlit pillow the plain outline of his own thin hand. For the moment anyway he was Philip Hoyt, at home in Norwich Town, Connecticut. Smiling gently, he fell asleep, waking to see the sunshine dancing on his mirror and to hear Bridget stirring the fire below him in the kitchen. Soon he smelled the coffee and the bacon. Those at least were no dream, and flinging himself out of bed, he remembered only that he was young and hungry and that presently breakfast would be waiting on the long table in the bright dining-room.

But in a pitifully short time he was cast back again into that other fantastic life. He wrote Elizabeth to send him half a dozen white shirts, and all the linen collars that he owned. "It's getting 'ot down here," he explained, twitting her about her habit of dropping her *h*'s, which she had never learned to correct. She had been begging him to send her a lock of his hair, and he teased her about that too. "I can't very well," he had replied. "My hair borders on the short, as I have it filed about once a month. I will send you a piece of my scalp, perhaps, before I get back." But all his gaiety could not deceive her, nor for long brighten the dark horror in which she now lived her days and which increasingly invaded her nights with hideous and heartbreaking dreams. She never heard a step on the walk or the drive or a hand knocking at the door but that her face whitened, and she waited breathlessly for the news that "something had happened to Philip." Long before the day such news did arrive, she had rehearsed it bitterly again and again.

The first week in September she had a short note from him, dated Washington, and could not help smiling tremulously at some of it:

Dear Mother,

Last Sunday our Regt. was out on picket just outside of Fredericksburg. We were called in, the city was evacuated, we marched in the rain to Acquia Creek, got to Washington yesterday morning. We have had a tough old time. I have not changed my clothes for two weeks, have slept on the ground every night. The only result of this has been to produce "several" freckles on my benign mug. Our baggage is the Lord knows where. I came down this morning to purchase underclothes.

Philip Hoyt

Reading it many times, she finally folded it away in the envelope, thinking as she did so that those freckles would amuse Turner too. But neither of them suspected that this spirited little note was the gesture of farewell from their son.

The following week, after the Battle of Antietam, a list of the Connecticut dead and wounded was posted in the store on the Norwich Town Green as usual. Mary had skipped up around the corner to buy herself a bag of peppermint candy. Somebody said to her:

"Did you see your brother's name in the list of wounded?"

The little girl stood for a moment staring while the man's forefinger pointed out Philip's name. Then without a word she turned and sped for home. No one—not even any of the boys—could outrun Mary, and on that sultry afternoon, with such fright in her heart, her long, light legs and delicate, flying feet were more than ever like those of some panic-stricken little doe bounding over the pebbles down the dusty River Road. She burst into the kitchen, where her mother sat stirring something in a bowl.

"Philip!" Mary cried out in agony, her eyes streaming, her small mouth distorted. The spoon clattered into the bowl while Elizabeth looked back at her with an expression so strangely terrible to the child that she rushed across to her mother, and flinging her arms around her, screamed piercingly, "Only wounded, Mother, only wounded!"

"Glory be to God!" whimpered old Bridget, and laid a trembling hand on her mistress's arm.

But Elizabeth knew. Even while those two tried to calm her, and later, when Turner, himself sick with foreboding, tried to imagine a hundred comforting possibilities, and other women, her friends, came to the house with their words of encouragement, repeating that he was "only wounded"—through it all, the little Englishwoman knew that her boy's life was done.

Colonel Howland's letter to Turner a few days later served only to give a final twist to that knife which she had carried in her heart for so many months. Turner handed her the letter, but he could not bear to watch her read it. He turned away and covered his face with his hands while she sat in the big wing chair beside the library window. The mellow sunlight of the pollen-laden September day struck softly across her bent head and glistened in the slow tears that fell on the sheet of paper in her hand.

Near Sharpsburgh, Sept. 20th, 1861

My dear Hoyt,

It becomes my painful duty to send you the sad intelligence of Philip's death. We have had a constant succession of fights for the last ten days, and Philip was present during all of them. On Wednesday, the 17th., the battle was terrific, and the carnage awful. It commenced about sunrise, and lasted till about seven in the evening. About four in the afternoon, the division, consisting of my Brigade and one other, was ordered to charge up a hill. We did so, and gained the position which we held for some time, but were afterwards compelled to fall back.

It was just at this time that Philip fell. He was shot in four places—in the breast, in the abdomen, in the leg, and in the arm. From what I have been able to learn, he died in a few minutes after receiving the wound in the breast. We were forced back from the ground and were unable to bring away the dead or even the wounded. The next day we drove the enemy back and we found Philip's body, but the rebels had rifled it of everything except his pantaloons and his shirt.

I gave orders to have the body embalmed, if possible; if not, to be buried in the Sharpsburgh yard, and to have a board put up and marked so that the body could be removed. We had orders to move forward at once, and Corporal Bingham of Yantic was left, with four men, in charge of the body, which was later buried. . . .

Philip fell while bravely discharging his duty. I would write more, my dear friend, did I not know that any words of consolation at such a time as this would be useless. Give my love to Mrs. Hoyt.

Elizabeth did not know, and never wanted to know, where or what Sharpsburgh was. She only wanted Philip to be laid in the earth of home. Turner finally managed to accomplish this for her, though when the sealed coffin came to rest under its flag in the hall of the old house, it proved to bring only an additional and a terrifying sorrow. She begged piteously to have it opened for one more look at the face of the dead, a plea refused for obvious reasons but which seemed to her only to imply the uncertainty of everyone as to whether it was actually Philip who had come home. Day and night she knelt beside the coffin, her arms lying rigidly outstretched along the flag, a tortured and desperate figure. Only now and then she spoke, beseeching Turner to be merciful and let her see whether the man beneath the fast-locked cover was her own flesh and blood or some unknown soldier.

After the funeral, Turner himself appeared to share something of her pathetic obsession, and sought in every way he could to secure clear proof that he had indeed buried his own son. He went finally to Yantic, to the family of the young Corporal Joseph Bingham who had been left on the battlefield to guard Philip's body. They were kind people whose son had known Philip from the time both had been little boys running loose on the roads and greens at Bean Hill and Norwich Town. They promised to write Joseph for some word about those hours after Antietam which would set the minds of Elizabeth and Turner at rest. Joseph's reply came late in October.

Father asked me if I was shure that was Philip's body. I am just as shure as I am that I have two eyes, for I put him into the coffin and helped bury him. He looked as natural as life.

Give my best regards to his Father and Mother and tell them for me that if my word is good, that it was certainly Philip's body. It was the hardest day and a half work I ever done in my life. It was such hard work to get anything done, it was by mere chance that I got a coffin, then two of us had to carry it over to the battlefield where I had a guard over Philip's body, then I could get no teem for love or money, so four men, all I had, took it and carried it over to the burying ground. We could not go by the road, so we had to carry it over the fields but it was all done as careful as if he had been my own brother. You have no idea what a battlefield is after such a battle as we had the 18th. If I had not been lucky enough to have found a coffin I should have made a box myself for I should never have put him into the ground without a box.

From that honest, decent, and touching statement Elizabeth and Turner drew whatever comfort and assurance was possible to them.

Often Turner reviewed in his mind that last year of Philip's life, torturing himself with endless and cruel questions. What had he done or what had he not done that this might have been prevented? Had he interfered too much, or not enough? Could Howland be blamed? Suppose he had left Philip alone at the time that he had sent in his resignation? And always that final cry into loneliness—the fiercest and the saddest of all—could not Almighty God Himself have seen fit to spare Turner Hoyt's only son?

To find forgetfulness Turner plunged once more into the work of his own busy life, and in that feverish release he was more fortunate than Elizabeth. Her life had always been her household, and in her home now, at every hour of the day, at every turn, memories of the infant son, the small and the grown boy, sprang up around the simplest usual tasks to keep her raw and quivering. All the phrases of all the letters and remarks of friends and kin rang in her ears, loud and hollow and unconsoling:

"He died nobly in a great Cause."

"His was an honorable life and a glorious death."

"He was as good an officer as ever went onto a battlefield."

And so in honor of all that glory, for the remaining few years of her life she draped herself in black from head to foot. Little Mary, sitting beside her mother in the meetinghouse on Sundays, never forgot the look or the smell of that thick crape, nor how the weight of the long veil dragged her mother's head forward in a perpetual attitude of weary despair.

The winter set in, but Elizabeth never ceased her journeys to Philip's grave. This was not in the old buryingground behind the house, but about a mile away in the big new cemetery at a bend of the Yantic River. Sometimes the dusk drew down and the supper table would be laid, and Mary with her small, cold hands tightly clasped stood at a front window, her face pressed against the darkening pane, waiting and watching for her mother. At last old Bridget, her shawl over her trembling head, or Turner himself would start out into the night. They always knew where to look, and occasionally they met her on her way home. But more often than not they found her still beside the grave, stretched out on the bitter-cold ground, silently and almost senselessly abandoned to her grief. Once she returned with a slip of paper in her hand, which she carefully fitted into an envelope and put away in the attic with the packets of Philip's letters. She labeled it "Verses left on Philip's grave by an unknown hand."

Those little notations on her son's letters, and the stains of her tears on them, were almost all that Elizabeth left behind her when she died. Some profound desire to obliterate all reminders of her individual self possessed her during her last years. Several times Mary found her destroying her own pictures or her small personal belongings. She said to the troubled young girl:

"I don't want a single trace of me to remain."

Yet something either very strangely overlooked or forgotten did remain in this American home of "plain Elizabeth Dodd from Oxon, England." Hidden away in the attic were the small gray shoes that had been a part of her widow's sober marriage outfit—the narrow, square-toed, heelless shoes of 1840, with lacings up the gray cloth sides. Perhaps in the beginning, long years before, someone had told her that it brought you luck to keep your wedding shoes.

CHAPTER XII

MARY HOYT

AFTER Elizabeth's death, the town bided its time watchfully, confident that Turner Hoyt would marry again. Every so often some report of this nature would reach Mary. Without any hesitation she always carried the gossip directly to headquarters:

"Father, is it true that you are thinking of marrying again?" And his answer would be as direct as her question.

"Bless you, no, Mary." Sometimes he added with a grin, "Once is enough for any man."

He might well have remarked that he couldn't spare the time either for courting or for wedding. As for his household, from the time she was eighteen, after two years at the seminary in New Haven, Mary "ran things" to suit him and to make him comfortable. If he heard rumors that Mary had "immediate prospects," he ignored them or refused to take them seriously. It pleased him to hear young people in his house, and he never exerted any strict supervision. None seemed necessary, for the gatherings there were lively with much chatter and laughter, and usually singing. He had bought Mary a square piano, which stood in the parlor amid the mahogany and horsehair furniture and the marble-topped tables. Over the piano hung one of the steel engravings of which Turner was so fond, "Washington Irving and His Literary Friends at Sunnyside." The piano had keys of mother-of-pearl instead of ivory, and above the keyboard, set into the front, was a fanciful design of birds and flowers, also in mother-of-pearl.

Mary played accompaniments with considerable dash, and she enjoyed singing duets with Harry Leonard or Will Thorley. There was also a Mr. Beasley from Buffalo who visited in Norwich every year. Mr. Beasley had no voice for singing, but he gave hilarious "interpretations" of the characters of Dickens. Turner particularly enjoyed Mr. Beasley.

When Mary went out in the evening, she always stopped at the door of her father's room downstairs at the back of the house and called dutifully:

"Father, I'm going now with Harry Leonard." (Or it might be Will Thorley, or Stanley Farnsworth, or any one of the young men about Norwich.)

"Yes, yes, child, I know," he would reply a little impatiently, not even looking up from his cluttered desk. "Run along—and close the door after you."

She marveled sometimes at his confidence in her, being aware of the many parental suspicions and restraints that restricted the lives of her friends. Others marveled too, but if one of them, unusually daring, ventured to suggest that he allowed Mary a dangerous liberty, he dismissed the matter with the brusque remark:

"My daughter Mary can take care of herself."

In his life alone in this house with his daughter there was something like a curious repetition of the earlier years with his mother. Mary seemed to him to resemble Felicity far more than Elizabeth. She had her grandmother's proud bearing, her height and slenderness. She gave Turner the same unwavering devotion, and she also was shocked by his bursts of profanity, by the streak of racy coarseness in his nature, and by the politician's way he had of loosening all restraint on tongue and conduct—which both women would have called "standards"—in order to meet and mix freely with all kinds of people. Whenever he had started swearing in his vigorous, imaginative way, Felicity would rise from her chair and say:

"Turner—Turner—my son, my *son!*" and leave the room, her spine at its stiffest, her steps statelier even than usual. And so too, years afterward, when he would remark, slyly suggestive, to his daughter: "My dear Mary, you must learn to pray with the righteous and drink with the dry," she had ready for him the same glint in the eye, the same toss of the head.

"That's not my way, Father," she would reply coldly, and take her departure, much offended. No doubt when left to himself, Turner grinned sheepishly, not in the least subdued but nevertheless glad that a woman belonging to him had her own spirit and her own pride.

No ugly scar of stinginess had been laid on Turner by that pinched time of his youth, when of necessity he and Felicity had counted their pennies. He indulged every whim of Mary's to an almost ridiculous degree. He loved to see her decked out in the finery that his mother had lacked, and he would watch her happily from the window of his office when she drove into the town, her blue eyes shining, her little straw or fur bonnets set jauntily on the mass of brown hair with the red sparks in it, arranged in a "waterfall" at the back of her head. On these occasions she sometimes watched him, when he did not see her, as he went whisking along the street from his office to another, his hands full of papers. And afterward she would say to him reproachfully:

"Father, why *will* you wear those forlorn old clothes? There was I, all gotten up to kill, and you in patched trousers! I could see those patches all the way from the top of Main Street."

He would laugh, his eyes twinkling. He liked to have her scold him for such a reason, but he had no intention of giving up his comfortable old clothes to go about the streets dressed like a dandy. Fine feathers would be more likely to lose him votes than to gain them. It was this same instinct that when he was campaigning led him to drive through the country districts in the most dilapidated carriage he could find, behind a pair of horses more noticeable for gaunt strength than for beauty.

But all this had nothing to do with his daughter; she

must never be poor and patched, either in body or in spirit. Certainly to the other girls in Norwich her existence glowed with the enchantment of one whose cradle had been presided over entirely by good and generous fairies. She was young, pretty, and merry. She was her own mistress in her own home without having had to pay the dubious price of matrimony for such a position, although she could have had her pick of the Norwich beaux. And, in addition to all this, there was the splendor of her winters in Washington.

By that time Turner was a Congressman, and Mary always went with him each year to the national capital. What happened to her there amid all those worldly and exciting functions, stay-at-home Norwich could only conjecture. But they imagined that she cut quite a swath. They might have been surprised had they known that she often felt timid, far less assured than at home, and sometimes even bored. For all her good looks, high spirits, and dainty dresses, she had moments of miserable embarrassment when she realized that Congressman Hoyt's daughter Mary in Washington and Judge Hoyt's daughter Mamie in Connecticut were not quite the same one all-devastating young woman. If she happened to be seated at dinner between two European gentlemen neither of whom spoke English with any ease, she would begin to remember ruefully her seminary days in New Haven and her neglected books. She had had a way there of casting a contemptuous glance at any girl who might exclaim, "Oh, I always *must* keep up my French!" and replying, "I have all *I* can do to keep up my English." But in Washington she was forced to admit that French would have saved many an awkward situation. She might sit silently at such a dinner table, rather wistfully observing her cousin Louisa Hoyt, whose tongue was as glib and amusing in French or Italian as in her own language.

Mary was always impressed by Louisa. She had lived in Europe, she had been presented at the English Court, she had poise and cultivation. Moreover, she did not pretend to take anyone or anything too seriously, which Mary had found particularly helpful during her first experiences in Washington when she faced some formidable strangers. Although she tried to keep in mind her father's cynical remark that "Great people usually look pretty small when you get close to them," it was Louisa, charming, tactful, and quick-witted, who guided and sustained her, and who did so quite painlessly. Louisa's face was small, plain, and spinsterish, but the eyes behind the glasses of her pince-nez never grew dull, and her figure, though short and slight, had its own distinction. She rode a horse to perfection—the stronger and more spirited the mount, the better. No matter how it challenged her courage and skill, she would return to the house as she had set forth, her broadcloth skirt sweeping back from the toe of her polished boot, her tall hat with its veil calmly afloat, still the undaunted Louisa, serene, amused, and perfectly soignée.

Probably Louisa was just one more instance of what seemed like Mary's unvarying good fortune. Louisa's father was Harrison Hoyt—that same Harrison who had been at the Bacon Academy in Colchester with Turner so many years before. A Chief Justice and a widower, he lived alone with his daughter, as Turner did with Mary.

For several seasons the quartet tried the rather dangerous experiment of sharing the same house. It was a success, and they were all very jolly and contented together. Since there were two Mr. Hoyts, Louisa called her father "Primus" and Turner "Secundus." When the two young women would come down the broad stairs arm in arm, dressed for the evening, their trains rustling behind them, the two old gentlemen would stand at the foot watching, devoted and possessive and more than a little delighted that they had so much youth and vitality to lead them around, as they were fond of saying, "by the nose." They would nudge each other slyly.

"Well, Primus, you're not at all proud of that girl of yours, are you?"

"No, Secundus, not any more than you are of yours."

So they would all drive off together to some party that afterward Mary and Louisa had the fun of discussing at home as intimately as if they had been sisters—whether they liked the collation, which women had been the most fashionably or the most scandalously dressed, what man had been the handsomest and the best dancer. For once the music started, Mary could happily forget her ignorance of foreign tongues. She could dance in any language, and whatever land he hailed from, she knew a handsome man when she saw one.

Sometimes in summer Louisa came to stay in Norwich Town for a while, but usually she returned to her beloved France. However, there were other visitors to help Mary through the days, which seemed drowsy though somehow comfortable after the gaieties of Washington. Mary always waited most impatiently for Miss Alethea Crewe from Brooklyn, whose aunt and uncle lived down on Washington Street. The two girls had been friends since childhood, when they first began calling each other Allie and Mamie. There was not much for them to do except drive off over the hills behind Charlie, or sometimes with Will Thorley and Harry Leonard, whose horses and carriages were far more elegant than Judge Hoyt's. And Allie liked to leave her aunt's home at odd times to go up and stay in the old house in Norwich Town, when perhaps there would be a picnic on Wawecus Hill, or a singing party around the piano, or even just the Sunday-night service in the meetinghouse on the Green. Really, what she enjoyed was being alone with Mamie in a place where there were no older women to supervise their pleasures, or to eavesdrop when they held those long conversations late at night upstairs in the front bedroom.

They liked to watch each other undress while they exchanged small, personal secrets. Mamie admired Allie's short golden hair that curled naturally; her own was straight, and so long and thick that she had to lift it up like a piece of silky cloth when she sat down at the dressing-table. It was difficult to arrange even with the help of curling tongs, pins, and nets, but Allie always sighed enviously as she saw her friend brushing it out. Allie was shorter than Mamie, and she had curves where curves should be, so that she plumped out a tightly buttoned bodice very properly and graciously. Mamie, on the other hand, was so virginal that she found it necessary to resort to the subterfuge of gathered lace sewed inside the front of her waists.

"Oh, Allie, you have such a perfect bust!" she would lament. "And just look at me. I'm nothing but crackers on a shingle!"

They often discussed marriage, and they were of one mind that there was little in it. Nothing, in fact. It was just some sort of cowardly confession of defeat. But it was an ever present menace, they agreed, and you must exercise constant watchfulness as well as courage, or you would be done for.

"I tell you what I think, Mamie," Allie said once very seriously. "I think if you can stick it out till you're thirty, you're safe."

"Yes, you're right, Allie. After you're thirty nothing can happen to you," replied Mamie.

Both relapsed into a prolonged and silent meditation upon that mystic year which would so mysteriously but inevitably mark the beginning of all peace and the end of all peril. After a while Mamie drew a deep breath.

"Well, anyway, Allie, I could never marry anyone in Norwich. I just *couldn't* marry someone I'd always known —just some fellow who's always called me by my first name."

Mary had been troubled sometimes by those fellows. Most of them, though adoring, held her in considerable awe, for behind her easy friendliness of manner there was a firm, shining core of sternness, an untouchable quality that kept them at a distance. Except in a dance, Will Thorley and Harry Leonard would not have dared to try to embrace her. But Stanley Farnsworth, the spoiled grandson of a man who had made a fortune out of a cough medicine, had been tempted too far one time by Mary's enchanting face. He had tried to kiss her one afternoon in Lover's Lane, where they were buggy-riding. Mary slapped his face, and slapped it hard enough to split her glove, and Stanley's gray topper rolled out into the dust. He was so startled that he jerked the reins and pulled his horse up short, whereupon Mary, gathering up her skirts, jumped out and flounced away toward home.

Muttering to himself, Stanley leaned out of the buggy to stare after her. Mamie was good and mad all right. He could tell that by the way her bustle bounced, and when presently she snapped open her parasol, the sharp sound echoed all through the quiet woods. Even the horse turned his head, his ears pricked and his eye rolling. What ailed the girl, anyway? He had only meant a bit of fun. Why did she go riding with a fellow and smile at him so prettily if she didn't expect him to make advances? Still grumbling, he got out and retrieved his hat. Driving home slowly by way of the Falls, he finally surmised that some girls liked kissing and some didn't. Well, if Mamie didn't, she didn't. Damn it all, he admired her, peppery though she was! He *respected* her, yes, by God, he did! And he'd be a gentleman about this. He'd make her a present, something costly that would knock her eye out. He guessed she wouldn't slap him for that! This made him feel brighter, and his face stung less as he drove into his big stable behind his red-brick house on Broadway.

Meanwhile Mamie had been muttering too. Whatever had got into Stanley Farnsworth? What did he think she was made of? How coarse and disgusting! How loathsome a man's great face was when it came so close, and you could feel, almost *smell* his hot breath! She shivered, though it was hot walking in the bright road and her anger made her even warmer. She glanced at her ruined glove disdainfully with eyes aglisten with indignant tears. When she crossed the railroad tracks, she stubbed her toe, which vexed her even more. On the bridge she stamped, not only to shake the dust from her little boots but to relieve her feelings as well.

A fool, that's what Stanley Farnsworth was; no, a cad—no, even worse, a *libertine!* But that shocked her a little. What a dreadful word, "libertine"! So dreadful, in fact, that it contained some implication of dim glamour which made it too flattering for that low, common Stanley Farnsworth. He was just nothing but a mushy ass! What would her father say if he knew about this? She mustn't tell him. She would just never speak to Stanley Farnsworth again, just never speak. Once more at home, she took off her dress, and moistened a handkerchief with some perfume from a small glass bottle labeled "Ocean Spray." Pressing this to her forehead, she lay down on the bed. By that time she had decided that though she would never speak to Stanley again, she would after a while bow to him on the street, but only coldly and from a distance.

Some days later a small package was brought to the house by the Farnsworth coachman. Mary opened the wrapping to find a circular case of pale-blue plush. Inside, reposing upon a bed of white satin, lay a brooch in the form of a fluted shell. On the shell's upper curve was a large, lustrous pearl, and supposedly crawling toward it was a ruby bug whose sides were studded with diamonds. Mary surveyed this jeweled arrangement with astonishment while she fingered Stanley's card, which bore no message—only his elegantly engraved name. It was obviously a peace offering in the vulgar creature's most florid style.

"Mercy," said Mary to herself, "what a thing! It looks just like the Farnsworth family!" Then her face broke into a mischievous smile. "I suppose I'm the pearl and he's the bug. Or is he trying to imply that my price is certainly not above rubies?" She tossed her head a little, and her eyes darkened. "Well, it is, Mr. Stanley Farnsworth, it *is*," she whispered, and replaced the plush cover with a firm, decisive gesture. Before evening the package had been returned to the red-brick house on Broadway, and a rueful Stanley, scratching his puzzled head, had decided that Mamie Hoyt was utterly beyond his comprehension.

Mamie and Allie both reached twenty-six in the summer of 1879. Only four more years of adamant stony-heartedness remained to each of them before their final escape into immaculate spinsterhood. They seemed very restless that summer, as though their vigilance had begun to wear on them. They were tired of doing the same things with the same people. They knew all Will Thorley's old jokes and Harry Leonard's new songs. Mr. Beasley had gone to California, and he sent them a photograph of himself, sitting in profile with field glasses in his hand gazing through a large window at a view of the Golden Gate. Or was it a framed painting? They couldn't decide. Anyway, it was inscribed "Your devoted Beasley, looking at the Golden Gate."

In July the roads shimmered with heat, the dust was as white and fine as flour, weeds wilted in the cracking ditches, and here and there in the shorn meadows the solitary elms stood motionless, their branches drooping with mournful grace. The thought of driving out over the hills became irksome, so Will and Harry suggested an expedition to New London on the steamer *Bella.* They went, but it all fell rather flat. The *Bella's* big wheels churned the glassy river with a cool sound, but there was no breeze and the hills on either side looked parched and dreary. In New London they had a tintype taken in a group. The girls wore the men's hats, and the men, sitting at their feet, wore the girls'. But it was too hot to be successfully silly, and if a violent thunderstorm had not broken over them on the trip home, the day might have ended in dismal silence, or even in some snappish dispute.

However, it may have been the *Bella,* swinging heavily away from the dock at New London to head down the harbor on her way toward the Sound and over to Block Island, which gave Mary the idea of going there. A day or two later she and Allie announced to their families that they intended to spend the month of August on Block Island. Neither the Crewes nor Turner made any objection. Everybody knew about Block Island. There were other Norwich people staying there, and the *Bella* was as safe and reliable as the horsecar that went back and forth between the Park and Franklin Square.

It happened that neither Mary nor Alethea had ever taken this trip. They carried their smelling-salts with them because Will Thorley meanly prophesied that seasickness was inevitable. He said that even General Grant, who once spent a day on the island, never returned there because he could not face the thought of encountering such rough weather a second time. But undaunted by the

General's defeat, the girls set forth, and their courage was rewarded by a placid and uneventful sail.

When the *Bella* left New London, they felt that they were really started, and sitting on the deck, they watched the familiar landmarks recede into the softening haze—the Groton Monument, the old fort, and the lighthouse on the point. They had brought a basket lunch from home, some sandwiches and cookies and a bottle of cold coffee. When they had finished these refreshments, they turned away from the brilliance of the blue water, and Mary took in her hand a small pamphlet that Harry Leonard had given her just before their departure from the Norwich dock. Allie yawned lazily, closed her eyes, and said, "You read to me, Mamie." Mamie began:

"*'Block Island; a Hand-Book, with a Map, for the guidance of summer visitors, telling how to reach that pleasant little place of resort, and what to do on getting there; together with description and sentiment calculated to adorn an otherwise plain tale, and to excite the interest of the apathetic, yet without too widely departing from the strict truth. By "Ben Mush," Staff Correspondent of the Norwich Morning Bulletin.'*"

"Do you know Mr. Mush?" inquired Allie.

"I know several," replied Mamie cryptically, and hastened to proceed.

"The first section is called 'Why Go to a Summer Resort at All?' and the second, 'Why Go to Block Island?' "

"Are you sure that's not just a book of conundrums?" said Allie, yawning once more.

Mary turned the pages slowly and meditatively, her own face a little sleepy-looking. Finally she said:

"I'll just read you a sentence here and there. . . . 'He, who loves to commune with nature, as well as with his fellow man, and seeks the refreshment and renovation of his soul as well as of his body, has here the restless, changeable, now soothingly quiet, now magnificently tumultous sea, gorgeous sunsets, and wide-spreading views, gently undulating meadows, and some grand and picturesque cliffs. . . . One can make as much of a hermit of himself as he likes; yet most excellent society is to be found, Philadelphia, Chicago, Buffalo, Troy, New York, and Boston, and many nearer centers of culture contributing largely to the floating population of the island; so that no one of true refinement and education can fail to find congenial company. . . . Block Island is a resort unusually free from the objectionable features of a fast American life. . . . Indeed the horse that can go more than four miles an hour yet remains to be discovered.' "

Allie's eyes opened full of suspicion.

"Mamie Hoyt, you made up that last sentence!"

"I did not, Allie Crewe. It's here in black and white. But since you don't trust me, I'll read the page on 'Appropriate Reading.' You must realize I couldn't cheat in such matters. I don't know enough." She opened the book and commenced again.

" 'At Block Island, people spend so much time in preparing for or dressing after the bath, on trips hither and thither on the water or ashore, in visiting with fellow idlers upon the broad veranda, in twilight reveries, in music or dancing, or in the more intellectual and social whist, with possible liquid accompaniments, that they have little time for reading. Yet everyone should bring a book or two, but be particular what he brings. Leave novels behind, leave everything in the way of study, leave philosophy.' "

"Ah," murmured Allie, "I've been wondering all day what it was I had left behind. But if it's only my philosophy . . ."

Mary disregarded her frivolity and continued to read doggedly:

" 'Take nothing but poetry, and that choose with care. The freedom here is especially favorable to the expansion of the esthetic instincts, and one soon finds his poetic nature quickened to a susceptibility almost unknown amid the pressing cares and occupations of ordinary life. Jean Ingelow's poetry is perhaps in feeling and description most in harmony with the spirit of the island. But Wordsworth and Tennyson will also be read here with a deeper tenderness and meaning, and Whittier's Tent on the Beach and the Wreck of the Palatine.' "

She stopped and waited a minute, but there was no response from her listener except gentle, regular breathing.

"You're asleep, Allie, aren't you?"

"Oh, no, no, not at all," said Allie, starting up and patting a curl into place under her hat. "Far from it. I am enjoying Mr. Mush very mush—*much*. And speaking of poetry, I think I'll get out my sewing."

She opened a small silk bag and drew out a lace-trimmed square of linen on which she was embroidering a picture of two grasshoppers holding a sheet of music and singing together. Behind them was a cluster of tall plumed grasses, and beneath, the inscription "In This Wheat Bye and Bye." Threading her needle with light green, she looked up expectantly.

"What, no more, Mamie?"

"Oh, a great deal more," replied Mamie. "What a stupid, silly subject poetry is! I'll find something more exciting. Listen, Allie, here's a paragraph about ourselves."

"Now, Mamie . . ."

"Yes, it is. Mr. Mush describes us with pitiless accuracy. He tells about the various other kinds of people who go to Block Island. And then this is what he says about us. 'There are, too, the butterflies of fashion, who seek to know what flowers of idle pleasure, folly and excitement bloom without the too familiar pale of local society; the designing mothers of marriageable daughters; the designing daughters, whose mothers let them go alone . . .' "

"Can there be any such?" said Allie.

" '. . . the impecunious and designing but otherwise eligible young man; and even more artful adventurers of both sexes, who thrive upon the weaknesses of mankind, and go to places of *rendez-vous* for their prey.' "

They both laughed.

"Is it possible," remarked Allie, "that after all this Block Island is a dark, wicked, and dangerous place?"

They were soon to know, for now the island was in sight, and they followed the other passengers forward to get a better view. At first they were depressed by the landing, and its surrounding clutter of fish-curing houses made them wrinkle their noses with distaste. But once in the carriage on their way to the hotel, they regained their spirits. The rough sandy road jolted them on the hard seats, but the air from the sea sparkled, and off across the unshaded meadows they saw a windmill against the sky. Their hotel, a gaunt wooden building, undecorated except for the American flag flying from the roof of the porch, stood on a breezy bluff. Their rooms were plain but tidy, the matting smelled new, and the china pitchers and bowls on the washstands were decorated with a neat pattern of small pink roses.

Mary and Alethea spent the first few days in contented indolence. Part of the time fog engulfed the island, so that they found it pleasanter to stay in the hotel parlor writing letters or chatting with acquaintances. Nothing could be seen beyond the veranda, which dripped with moisture, nothing heard except the foghorn sounding dismally at intervals.

When the first clear morning came, the two girls rushed off to the beach. In their genteel dark, heavy bathing-dresses with ruffled bloomers and black stockings, they found the sun almost too hot, and they went immediately into the water. Neither could swim beyond a few hasty breast strokes taken with the chin lifted anxiously above the ripples in shallow water. And after each such effort they staggered to their feet for a gasping moment, usually clutching at each other with shrill cries, for they were afraid of the surf.

They were sitting resting at the foam's edge when Mary first saw John Hale walking down the sand. She did not then know who he was. She only knew that he was the handsomest man she had ever seen. In his black bathing-suit, with sleeves just falling over his broad shoulders, and long hose that modestly covered even his feet, he looked something like an elegant young acrobat who had just swung down from his trapeze. It was not an easy costume to wear, and it had made many men ridiculous in Mary's eyes. But as she stared spellbound at this tall stranger, his dark head held in so knightly a way, at the strength and the shapeliness of his whole body, he looked anything but undignified. She even began to wonder, very fancifully, how it would have seemed to meet a man with legs like those, dressed in rich colors, on the steps of a medieval castle. Or did he belong in some future romantic time? Certainly his kind of beauty was exiled on this New England island in the year 1879.

Alethea had turned toward him too, but he did not so much as glance at them, though finally he came to stand near by, looking eagerly out to sea. Mary saw his face then, almost a boy's face, ardent and defenseless, a little shadowed by some dream. He went swiftly down to the water and dove in, vanishing with effortless ease under the crest of a huge wave, and swimming out so far that his head was only a dark speck on the brilliant blue.

They did not see him again until dinnertime. By then they had learned who he was, that he had just arrived from his home in Glastonbury, Connecticut, and that he planned to spend every day fishing far off the island with one of the old captains at the wharf, a crony of his previous summers. During dinner Mary found herself often glancing in his direction. Once, for a moment, he returned her gaze. She was accustomed to being stared at, but it was unusual for the man's eyes to turn away first, as John Hale's did. It nettled her a little.

The following evening the waitress bustled to their table

with two plates of steaming bluefish—some of Mr. Hale's catch, and sent with his compliments. They bowed to him across the room, and he smiled. It would be easy after that, Mary thought, but she was mistaken. For one thing, John Hale didn't dance. Mary and Alethea could scarcely credit such a statement. A good-looking man who didn't dance! Who ever heard of such an anomaly? But John Hale insisted that he just didn't care about dancing. Later he made a different explanation to Mary. He was idealistic about women, and taking hold of a girl and swinging her around a room seemed to him unchivalrous. Usually, after dinner when the music started, he sat by himself quietly with a book, or sometimes played a game of billiards with other men. Mary saw him once or twice standing in the doorway gravely regarding the dancers, but he soon went away. She thought him rather unreasonable.

One evening Allie found that Mary had disappeared. None of the dancers knew where she was, but someone playing whist in the parlor said she had gone sailing with John Hale. This startled Allie, and she even went out alone to stumble along the stony bluff, hoping for some sign of the couple. It was a moonless night, but the sky was softly radiant with stars, and the surf sucked more gently than usual around the pebbles on the shore. Allie said to herself anxiously, "It's too *dark* to go sailing." But when Mary returned she said they had gone because it *was* dark. They wanted to see the phosphorescence in the water, and you couldn't see it so well when the moon shone. On other nights, however, when the moon did shine, they forgot about the phosphorescence and went sailing to see the moon.

John began to neglect his daily fishing expeditions. Instead he drove Mary all over the island, to the cliffs and the lighthouses, across the low, rolling meadows where the fleecy summer clouds, heaped in the sky, drew their slowly traveling shadows. On one of these drives he asked diffidently if he might call her by her first name. She nodded graciously.

"Call me Mamie. All my friends do."

But he frowned and shook his head.

"Oh, no, I couldn't do that. I hate to hear you called that. It doesn't suit you at all. Not Mary either—I've known so many Marys. I'd like to call you Molly." She smiled at him, very much pleased with his idea. Then he added seriously: "But nobody else must call you Molly. That's *my* name for you."

Sometimes they walked along the beach or made themselves comfortable against a rock with shawls and an old coat of John's. Allie, strolling with another lady, came upon them one afternoon under the bluff where they were sitting (much too close together, she thought severely), Mary with her hands clasped behind her head, watching the waves breaking and falling, John reading to her from a small volume that looked as if it might be poetry. Allie passed them rather stiffly, exchanging only a word or two. *Poetry,* she was thinking in disgust, and Mamie, Mamie of all people, listening, patient as Grief on a monument!

Mamie had always had beaux hanging around her. Allie was used to that, but she uneasily recognized a different quality in this man's attentions and, even more disturbing, a gentler attitude in Mamie's reception of those attentions. Moreover, she began to feel a certain wariness in Mamie when they were alone together, a withdrawal of that complete confidence which they had always shared. Allie decidedly did not like the look of things, but she did not speak out until the forenoon when she happened on Mamie standing on the deserted veranda with John Hale's cane. She was holding the handle against her face, and Allie suspected that she was kissing it. At Allie's horrified expression Mamie flamed with guilt, but she was too proud to explain, realizing perhaps that the explanation would hardly placate Allie. It was not the first time she had smelled the intoxicating combination of expensive cologne and good tobacco that John Hale's hand left on the gold head of his cane. It was a male smell, clean, strong, and luxurious, and it fascinated her. But nothing could induce her to confess as much to Allie, who now faced her so accusingly and said in a low tone:

"Mamie Hoyt, you're falling in love with that fellow!"

Mamie remained silent a moment, then she said rather haughtily, "You assume too much, Allie." But this was no denial, and Allie moaned faintly. "We must go home right away," she whispered desperately. "We must go home, or it will be too late."

"Too late," thought Mary strangely to herself. "Doesn't she know it was too late the day that I was born?"

The color faded from her cheeks, and she looked at Allie sadly, almost beseechingly. She would have spoken, but just then two elderly ladies with their knitting ambled around the corner of the veranda, and both Mamie and Allie fled into the hotel. Allie went up to her room at once and commenced to pack feverishly. But when Mamie came in she only said quietly:

"You can go if you like, Allie, but I propose to stay."

Allie straightened up from the trunk, aghast. "Why, you can't do such a thing! Stay on alone with that man! What will people say?"

"I won't be alone with anyone, Allie. And I don't care what people say."

They were both trembling a little now, both determined not to cry. Allie, choking back a sob, said: "What will your *father* say to all this? Or don't you care about *that* either?"

Mary turned quickly and left her. The thought of her father had been like a sharp stone in her breast for many days. It bruised her even while she was in John's arms, looking into his dark eyes. And at night, turn and twist as she might, there was no rest from the smarting remembrance of that stormy, unpredictable, loyal man who waited for her to come back, whose letters told how much he missed her and cared for her, who gave to her so lavishly but who expected in return her single-hearted devotion and her undivided life. Allie, with the cruel marksmanship of an intimate friend, had known just where Mamie's heart was still most vulnerable, and had shot her arrow home with savage skill.

Nevertheless, Mary stood her ground. The following morning Allie departed alone on the morning boat. Mamie went down to see her go, the behavior on both sides admirably polite and self-controlled. Only when the sea widened between the two women, one standing rigidly on the stern deck of the *Bella,* the other alone on a corner of the dock, did the tears begin to flow. But then they could not see each other's grief, and neither one would wave.

Allie, shading her eyes with her hand and watching that wind-blown solitary figure, thought for one wild moment that she would jump into the water. Why had she deserted Mamie like that? But she had supposed, up to the last moment, that the stubborn girl would relent and go too. What had they said, laughing, on the way over, when they read Ben Mush's silly book—that the island might prove to be a dangerous place? Well, it was dangerous. It was fatal. It had destroyed Mamie. Oh, what *had* happened to her—Mamie, the militant virgin, the scoffer, the jester, the spurner of men's offers? What had silenced her flippant tongue and her frivolous words? She had been so gay, so spirited a defender of maidenhood, her weapons so honorable, her courage so enduring, her strength seemingly so invincible.

"Oh, Mamie, Mamie, Mamie!" cried Allie through her tears, as though she were calling to the dead.

Yet somehow that last sight of Mamie, standing in her white dress in the wind and the sun, was anything but an image of defeat. Rather she looked like a figurehead on a ship, able to breast the darkest wave and the most stinging spray.

With Allie gone, it seemed to Mary as though the sea closed in on John Hale and herself. She walked among other people as if they were shadows, startled if they spoke to her, sometimes not even answering, conscious only of her own flesh and blood and John's, and of the island itself, set in a ring of white foam that had a sound like the beating of her own heart. She heard the sea now as she had never heard it before. Night after night she sat wakeful at the window of her little, bleak room, watching that waste of water as it moved dimly under the brilliant net of white stars, shaping and reshaping the shore.

There were times when she too, like Allie, wondered sadly what had happened to Mary Hoyt, that Mary who had never meant to give herself wholly to any man, who because she knew nothing of tenderness and passion, had been so blithely certain she would never need or desire them. Was it years ago, or only this afternoon, that so proud a girl had so innocently set her foot upon this island in the sea? Sitting there in the dark, she would cry for that girl, but each time the tears started falling on her hand she was reminded of John's face and John's voice as he read to her:

> Tears, idle tears, I know not what they mean,
> Tears from the depths of some divine despair
> Rise in the heart and gather to the eyes,
> In looking on the happy autumn-fields,
> And thinking of the days that are no more.

She could not remember the lines without seeing John's sweet and rather sensuous mouth, and the thick lashes lying so darkly on his sunburnt cheeks. Mary had never listened to poetry except as her father quoted Shakespeare and the Bible with flashing eyes and flourishing gestures, or when Mr. Beasley sometimes replaced Dickens with sentimental recitations. But John Hale read verse as simply and seriously as if it were the natural utterance of his own heart:

> Dear as remembered kisses after death,
> And sweet as those by hopeless fancy feigned
> On lips that are for others; deep as love,
> Deep as first love and wild with all regret;
> O Death in Life, the days that are no more!

It was the days that are no more which made the poem so unbearably sad to Mary. Those were the years with her father which the coming years with John would end—must end. And if she had already, in a sense, painfully parted with herself, she must do so all over again in parting with her father. She wondered a great deal about the old man and the young man, how they would meet, what they would say to each other, whether they would be enemies or friends. They were alike in only one way. Both of them loved Mary Hoyt and wanted her to keep.

In that last week together on the island, Mary Hoyt and John Hale became the scandal of the hotel. They were gone, out of sight for long hours, nobody knew where. Even in the last few days, when fog drew in, they were not seen in the hotel parlors, where the other guests, bored and inactive, gathered to gossip about them. They went down on the beach to wander in a world as mysterious as the hollow of a white shell, and noiseless except for the muffled beat of the water and its long slide up the grating sand. Nobody was surprised when they left together on the same boat. They stood with their hands clasped looking back as they sailed away, but their shore was lost in mist. Even that low, pursuing sound of waves breaking on gray crags softened more and more into something like a dream dreamed long ago. Their island might as well never have existed at all.

John went directly home to Norwich Town with Mary to meet Turner. But Turner did not need to be told. Even if he had not already talked with Alethea, he would have known when he saw his daughter standing beside the man she had chosen.

"Well, child, it's all for the best," he said quietly. But Mary wept as though her heart would break.

Turner liked John Hale from the first, but he did not leave it at that. Immediately he sent letters flying all over Connecticut to get the opinions of others. He could not help rejoicing that John planned to follow his own profession; the young man told him that he had recently passed his bar examinations and expected to commence practicing in Hartford in the fall. It disappointed him that John was a Democrat, and he felt it a mistake for him to be an Episcopalian, but neither of these matters aggravated him to the extent that Mary's friends were aggravated when they learned that she had engaged herself to someone "from away," and that he was a Harvard man. Will Thorley, Harry Leonard, Stanley Farnsworth, and even Mr. Beasley had all gone to Yale.

Early in the fall Turner and Mary went up to Glastonbury for a short visit to meet John's sisters. Already they had written her elegantly phrased little notes, perfectly courteous but slightly chilly. And they too, like Turner, had made inquiries throughout the state about Judge Hoyt's daughter. John's selection of a suitable wife interested them all profoundly. They felt that the fate of the Hale family, the continuance of the name and the blood, hung on John's marriage, for his three older brothers were dead.

Eliza and Sara lived near by with their families, so they drove out to the old home to help Sophia, the one spinster sister, greet her guests. Lucy, married to a Southerner, could only write urgent and lengthy letters about the affair. All three sisters had married Episcopal clergymen, but in spite of their state as wives, somehow retained much of the quality of maiden ladies, as if espousals with men of God did not tend to coarsen as much as common matings with inferior persons.

Mary had confronted Presidents and ambassadors in Washington with less trepidation than she felt in facing these staid, dignified women standing amid their solid mahogany and their heavy silver. But when Turner, with his consummate tact, remarked that he had known their father Thaddeus Hale when they were both in the Connecticut Legislature, the stiffness in their spines and voices relented. They led the way at once to their father's portrait, where they all chatted together reminiscently.

Mary studied the portrait, looking in vain for any resemblance to John. The face was narrow, ruddy, and somewhat severe, the blue eyes gazed out steadily and a little coldly. When she heard his daughters reminding each other how he would say to his children, "Always get up from the table hungry," she could well believe it. He had too purposeful as well as too fastidious an air for a man given to excesses. The portrait of his lady hung beside his, and there Mary found John's dark eyes and delicately molded mouth. But nobody mentioned these likenesses. The daughters, like all New England women, concentrated on the males, and implied that John was in every way the son of Thaddeus.

Turner became a little restless on this visit. He valued and admired the gentility of these women, the ancientness of their house—which antedated his own—and the extent of the wide lands that had always been theirs since they were purchased from the Indians in the seventeenth century. He realized that in this place, this clan, he was indeed face to face with all that he implied when he talked of "old Connecticut." But he himself was gay and vivacious, he liked to wave his hands and guffaw loudly when he told his outrageous stories, and so much sobriety of manner depressed him. It subdued Mary, too. She wondered if there had ever been any uproar in this house, as there was often at home when her father gave way to some outburst. Even singing anything but hymns in these immaculate rooms would be unseemly. Life here day after day, she thought, would take the tone of a mellow old bell—somber, sweet, and grave. But she could not imagine herself taking part in it.

During the visit nothing was said about setting a definite date for the wedding. Perhaps John's sisters, like Allie Crewe, thought that the engagement would not "last." Allie had said, "This all happened very quickly, Mamie—a little too quickly, in my opinion, to last."

After the Hoyts and the married sisters had gone, John and Sophia settled back once more into the quiet existence they had shared since the death of their father. Sophia was so much older than John that she had always felt somewhat motherly toward him. Now she felt it her duty to try to draw him out about Mary. One evening when they were sitting in the small room that had been Thaddeus's study, she with her knitting, he with a book, Sophia said softly:

"Miss Hoyt is a handsome woman, John."

"I think so," said John, not looking up from his book.

"She dresses very fashionably," continued Sophia. As this drew no response, she ventured a little further. "Is she considered somewhat extravagant?"

"I like to see a woman well dressed, Sophia," replied John, still reading.

There was a pause during which Sophia, not sure whether she had been rebuffed or not, decided to change her tactics.

"She is not of the Church."

"No," said John, and added, a little reluctantly, as if he were afraid of betraying some confidence of Mary's, "but she is greatly attracted by the service."

Something in the atmosphere of the room seemed to relax slightly, and the next silence was less guarded. Presently Sophia sighed as she completed a row of her knitting and stopped to contemplate the stitches.

"Ah well," she remarked, "marriage often changes a woman."

She was, possibly, merely hopeful for Mary's conversion, but John chose to infer more criticism. He lifted his eyes from his book at last, and looked directly at his sister as he said quietly: "I wouldn't want Molly changed in any way."

Sophia said no more. However, if she could have guessed at this time that John even considered living away from Glastonbury after his marriage, she would have spoken on endlessly and earnestly. She thought of course that the bride would be brought home to the old rooftree, and that she would continue to live there herself too, as she always had done. But if John owned an old house with a spinster sister queening it within, Mary also possessed an old house where her widower father had long reigned as king. They saw almost immediately that they must commence their own life together somewhere outside of Connecticut.

Also John now decided that after all it was a tedious business starting as a lawyer. He ought to find something that would be more profitable in a shorter time. His first experiment was investing in a woolen mill. When this ended disastrously, he interested himself in a paper mill with offices in Boston. There for a time it seemed as though he had found the prosperous solution, not only for his finances but for the problem of founding his own home with Mary away from relatives. So it was two years before their marriage took place, during which time the engagement, in spite of all ominous prophecies, "lasted."

Mary and John planned for themselves the simplest kind of a ceremony, but Turner circumvented their modest intentions. Little by little, somewhat to their astonishment, they saw their nuptials develop into more and more of a political gathering. Mary remained determined against the inclusion of any of "Father's Greek friends," but having won that point, she was unable to withstand his arguments in favor of having the Governor and his staff, and other state figures who meant nothing to her or to John as people and whose presence at their wedding seemed somehow grotesque. But in the end she allowed

Turner his own way in almost every direction. After all, she thought, it was the last gesture he could make for his daughter as Miss Mary Hoyt, and she might as well let it be a sweeping one, wide enough not only for his love of her but also for his pride in himself.

Cousin Louisa wrote from Washington very gracious and interested letters about Mary's wedding-dress. She thought it would be a pity to have it made in Norwich. So Mary was persuaded to come down for a visit, and together they conferred with Louisa's French dressmaker. Hours of discussion were spent over satin flutings, pearl edgings, lace sleeves, and a Medici collar. Eventually the dress had all four, and was very regal.

But on the evening of the wedding Mary's bouquet caused more murmurs of surprise than her dress. Although it was October, when the yellowing gardens were bare except for the bitter-scented asters and chrysanthemums, she carried white spring blossoms in her hand. John had once heard her say that her favorite flower was the narcissus, and so in spite of the raising of four sisters' eyebrows at such an expensive fancy, he arranged that Mary should have what she loved.

The sisters, supported by each other and also by quite a contingent of outlying kin, carried themselves nobly throughout the ceremony in the church and the following reception at home. Only once Eliza and Sophia bent their heads together for a private comment. Sarah and Lucy surmised that it was something good, and clustered near for its repetition. Then Lucy had the temerity to whisper it into the very ear of the bridegroom. Even in the crowded room Mary did not fail to notice all this, and she asked

John what the secret was. He smiled with mild amusement.

"Oh, they just said they felt as though I had been married by a justice of the peace."

It was a typical Episcopalian comment on the bleak service of an unritualistic church, with a parson in a black coat instead of a clergyman in vestments. Instead of resenting it, Mary knew exactly what they meant. She had never really been at home amid the stern, undecorated doctrines of the meetinghouse, and even before she knew John she had turned her eyes longingly toward the pageantry of his church. Now, standing beside him his bride of less than an hour, these rather caustic words of her sisters-in-law stirred in her an odd regretfulness. She wished her wedding night have been different, that its memory some day would not lack a rich and glowing beauty which she would so much like it to have.

Alethea Crewe was another who weathered the event with fortitude and calm. She was one of the six bridesmaids who were kept busy during the evening trying to thaw out the ushers, classmates of John's at Harvard and most of them Massachusetts men. For a time they seemed grimly determined not to forget that this was a Yale town in Connecticut, but such snobbishness seldom prevailed long against Turner's affability. He was always delighted to play the part of host, and he moved about the rooms of his old house, softly lit by many candles, slapping his Republican friends on the back, chuckling and saying:

"John has only one fault—he votes the wrong ticket."

Alethea also devoted a good deal of her attention to Will Thorley, Harry Leonard, and Stanley Farnsworth.

Stanley, who applied himself appreciatively to the punch bowl, became first an object of amusement and later a subject for concern. Will and Harry finally escorted him out into the frosty night, and ran him up and around the Norwich Town Green. On his return to the house he was able to agree with Alethea quite clearly, though perhaps a little too emphatically, that Mary Hoyt and John Hale were the handsomest couple who had ever been seen in Norwich.

So they were married and went away to Boston to live forever. Mary was to continue to be beautiful, beloved, and gay, and John was to make a fortune almost immediately. They were very happy as they set forth in that October of 1881, and deeply in love, and quite certain that their future would be an idyl, unshadowed, unembittered, and serene.

PART III

CHAPTER XIII

MARY HALE

OFTEN my mother seemed a little bewildered at the direction her life had taken, soaring out into an arc toward the unknown only to come back full circle again, home to Norwich Town. If someone spoke of Mary Hoyt or called her by that name, she would smile half sadly, half humorously, and say:

"Oh, Mary Hoyt—that girl. She's been dead for many a year."

But that Mary now and then haunted her, emerging

from the folds of some frilled and fragile dress when a trunk cover was lifted in the attic or from an old, fading tintype, or it was evoked—and then most strangely and incredibly of all—by some glance, word, or gesture from her sons or her daughter. One of us would catch her, grown suddenly pensive, a light veil of reverie momentarily cast across her crystal-clear blue eyes.

"If I had not married," she would say then slowly, "if I had never had you children, what would my life have been like? I wonder—I suppose I would have just lived on here with Father."

Her mind held steadfast to one certainty—that she could have had but the one husband that she did have. No other man but John Hale could have succeeded in persuading her that any destiny was preferable to "just living on with Father," or even possible.

On the whole, the Mary Hale who was my mother spoke very little of the earlier Mary. And if Mary Hoyt was not entirely dead—as many daily sparkling resurrections in my mother testified—at least she seemed to have been, for the most part, laid away in the attic, along with the trophies and the trinkets of her heyday. More than from my mother herself, I heard about her from others, although their picture of the vivacious figure holding the reins of her quick-stepping little horse, or of the gay girl—very quaintly clad, according to my ideas—who danced the night through, was a difficult one for me to place beside the soberer and statelier reality of my mother. For what I saw was a very handsome middle-aged woman whose whole devotion was given to just two absorbing interests, her home and her church.

In those days, in her kind of home there was a special quality drawn out of life and poured back into it, not only as a blessed libation on the family within the walls, but overflowing beyond them into the whole community wherever it was parched. If my mother was extravagant with money, she was no less so with herself, and there the wealth seemed inexhaustible. Being Mrs. John Hale, the daughter of Judge Hoyt, did not mean just the smug satisfaction of showing off heirlooms to her admiring acquaintances. It also included the responsibility of serving families who had been less fortunate than her own. Wherever there were new babies, or bedridden aged, or illnesses without comforts, or sudden and terrifying calamities among the poor of the neighborhood, those households never failed to hear my mother's knock on the door.

They knew well enough that she would not come dressed in her finery, merely to hand out cash and advice with a patronizing air. She arrived laden with food, liquor, medicines, and linens from her own stores and, taking off her hat and coat, she would set quietly to work at the nearest necessary task, whether it meant cleaning up a kitchen, rubbing an old colored man with alcohol, or remaking a bed under a child worn with fever. Awe of the lady who lived aloof amid her possessions was replaced by respect for the woman who could work with them and beside them so simply, so competently, and so tirelessly that her favors left no sting. Her charity was as much a part of her inheritance as her Chippendale chairs. Behind her stretched a line of women in whom compassion was so closely interwoven with pride as to be practically strands of the same thread. Even in their own less prosperous times, they had all gone about their countryside and their village streets with a full basket on a willing arm. It was in the tradition of the well-born to expect and to welcome the dependence of the ignorant, the needy, and the humble.

My mother received some quaint compliments and some queer adorations. Mrs. Halloran was an old, toothless Irishwoman from Bean Hill who sometimes did extra cleaning and cooking in the various houses near and around the Norwich Town Green. Once when at Miss Bateman's, she pointed through the trees in the direction of our house and remarked as she smacked her gums:

"That Mrs. Hale, now, ah, there's a one! She's got a sharrup eye for dir-r-t!"

And all one spring and summer a gawky, forlorn boy of eighteen appeared every morning to follow at my mother's heels as she went about her household duties. He was the son of a deacon in the Norwich Town meetinghouse, agonizing his way through an adolescence that had reached its peak of tragedy in his complete failure to pass his college entrance examinations. He never spoke to my mother of this. In fact he rarely spoke at all, but stood silently, first on one foot, then on the other, while she dusted here and there; or he plunged forward awkwardly to help her when she shook out a sheet or a pillow on the beds. He seemed at peace just to be near her and to watch her, particularly in the kitchen. There, if she happened to be mixing a cake, she always let him lick up what was left on the spoon and in the bowl, as if he had been a very little boy.

He knew his way around our pantry too, like many another young person in the neighborhood. Two big crocks especially for hungry children stood on a shelf under the china cupboard. One was always full of the spicy cookies called hermits, and the other held pastry shells, which we could fill ourselves with raspberry jam from the jar in the icebox. There too, if we were thirsty we never failed to find fresh milk in the big white jug with blue stripes running around it that somebody said looked just like a fat man in a bathing-suit.

On the other hand, my mother did not entirely escape encounters with hatred. The town was not lacking in spiteful minds and vindictive tongues, and her dignity and graciousness could not always save her from attacks, particularly as she sometimes, for one innocent reason or another, deliberately exposed herself to ill-nature. To strike through so well-armored a spirit as hers was not easy, but it was possible, and cruelly so, if anybody chose to be contemptible enough to use against her as a weapon the fact that her son Sam had a crooked back. There was one such person—wickedly enough, another woman. She lived across the river and had a small son who, probably with good reason, very often ran away from her. One afternoon, from a window my mother saw this woman beating the boy in the lane that led to the burying-ground. His cries were so pitiful and the punishment so prolonged that finally she could no longer bear it and, going out into the garden, spoke to the woman as quietly as she was able to in view of her resentment.

"Don't whip your boy like that any more," she said. "You might injure him for life."

The woman stood looking down at her, still clutching the stick, the child sobbing against her skirts.

"Well, you ought to know," she said, slowly and gloatingly. "You didn't have much luck with yourn."

The inference was unmistakable, and for once my mother's usually quick tongue was stilled. She gazed back at the hard, sneering face of that other mother, her eyes slowly filling with tears. Then she turned and went back into the house. But at least there was no more whipping that day. The woman disappeared, and the boy wandered away into the burying-ground, where perhaps he cried his heart out alone among the old graves.

That ancient cemetery knew more about the grief and the gaiety of children than any place among the living in the town. Whether a child went there by himself, looking for solace under the long gray-green leaves of the weeping willows that swayed in the breeze like seaweed under water, or whether he went with other children after flowers, or berries, or for a game of hide-and-seek, he need fear nothing from those who lay so quietly and so patiently beneath his scuffing feet. It was a safe place for us all to roam or to play. But then, what place did not seem safe? We were gone from home for long ecstatic hours, ranging from Plain Hill to Gulliver's Woods, to Mediterranean Lane, to Meeting House Rocks, to Wawecus Hill, down along the Yantic River to the Falls and Indian Leap, across to Green's Pond over beyond the Lowthorpe Meadows, up to Sentry Hill and beyond, and higher still to Gallows Hill, exploring a hundred and one nameless but beautiful brooks, bogs, groves, caves, pastures, and springs. Nobody, least of all my mother, seemed to worry about us or watched the clock or wondered, terrified, if we had been "run over," or drowned, or smashed by a fall from some high rock or tall tree, or stung to death by wasps or snakes, or lured away by wandering tramps into the woods for evil purposes. As a matter of fact, we came close enough to all those dangers. But we were tough and durable, and seemingly we were not afraid of wild creatures or deserted places. We kept our mouths shut when anything happened to us—particularly if it hurt—and we could run faster and farther than any other children I have ever known.

During one winter there seemed to be some anxiety among parents when we selected for our bobsleds a hilly road that crossed at its foot another road where the trolley cars came around a curve. But nobody was ever injured, probably because the motormen always stopped the cars to look, and then barely crept around the turn. And there was a legend that one summer the ice cart had run away, the horses plunging down the road where the children, out for recess from the Norwich Town school, were playing tag in front of the butcher shop. They had scattered to safety, but it was a haunting memory for some of the mothers. It did not seem possible that it had ever happened when we looked at the ice cart as it stood outside some house under the arching elms, waiting for the iceman to stagger in with the big white blocks clutched in the tongs. It was a shabby covered cart, open at the back, dripping drearily from its rear end, and on hot days the two big gray horses, who stood without hitching, wore straw hats, their ears poked through little holes in the straw. They seemed to find it a great effort merely to twitch a flank, and they often had to be clucked at cajolingly several times by the driver before they would move on heavily to the next stop. In the road where the cart had been would lie a small pile of chippings from the ice. We would pick up pieces, lick off the dirt, and suck them. They were very refreshing.

At the end of such blissful days we arrived home bedraggled, tired, hungry, covered with briers, burrs, or bruises, our knees or shins often glued to our stockings by some dark dried stain that might be either clotted blood or smashed fruit. We would have forgotten whether we had fallen on a rough spot or knelt in a soft one, and anyway it didn't much matter. We had had a good day. All we asked was plenty of supper and a long, deep sleep.

My mother would look at these tousled gypsies as they came banging in her back door, and send them upstairs to restore in themselves some resemblance to her own clean children. She did not forget at those times that she had been Mary Hoyt, and that Mary too had gone in and out of this same old house to run as wild as we did in these same fields.

I seemed to have an unlimited supply of fresh gingham dresses, and brown or black ribbed stockings, and little cotton drawers and petticoats trimmed with Hamburg edging. Ned was equally well equipped with his own sturdy pants, shirts, and shoes, though the problem of keeping him decently in order was more constant and also more complicated than in my case, because not only was his area of ranging far wider than mine, but his pursuits were more savage. His foraging yielded him such odd prizes as cows' eyes, carried in his pocket "for good luck," or frogs' legs brought home, also in his pocket, and then forgotten for so long that the result was painful to all.

Polliwogs' eggs, small turtles, pet crickets in little boxes with holes punched in the top for air, fireflies held captive under a glass, so you could watch them shining at night beside your bed, a chameleon bought at the county fair, with a little chain around his neck attached to a pin that you wore on your shoulder—we had them all. Ned, however, was not just a collector. He had the huntsman's hearty appetite that found any wild flavor palatable. So he brought home dead creatures as well as living, rabbits or gray squirrels for pies, and once he even hopefully inquired if crows were good to eat. When my father assured him that they were not, he shot them anyway, "just for practice." He had no use for crows, but their clever ways of outwitting him often challenged his pride.

Somehow he managed to capture one, and after clipping its wings, brought it home in a bag. That was a fall evening, and we were all at supper, having tired of waiting for him but knowing that he would turn up eventually. He came in at last, smelling of bonfires and frosty air, and dumped the crow out of the bag onto the dining-room floor. We had all been somewhat fearful that he might have a snake, but we were almost as startled to see the crow. The big black bird stood quite fearlessly on the rug, its sleek head on one side, squinting up at that laughing group of human beings in their warm, brightly lighted room. Its eyes shone uncannily, and after a cautious moment of inspection, it picked its way sedately around the table with an air of assurance not unmixed with contempt.

I think my mother did not like the sight of that wild creature who had been made so defenseless. More than anything else in nature, she loved birds. "Chris," the canary in his gilt cage that hung in a sunny window, was her own special delight and care. She bathed and fed him with devotion, and always seemed to be able to coax a ripple of song from his yellow throat even on his melancholy days. Sometimes she would let him out to fly around the room, but he never went very far away from her, watching for the moment when he could flutter to her outstretched hand and hopping up her arm, take a seed from her lips.

There were few pretentious festivities in our house. My mother and father never gave dinner parties, and neither of them cared for cards or, for that matter, any games. On the few occasions when they went out in the evening, Ned and I were awed by their appearance. They seemed to be setting forth, godlike, on some dazzling adventure beyond our imagination. It was almost impossible to believe that they would ever return from being persons of such resplendence and once more willingly resume their sober, parental disguise.

Mary Hoyt had been a girl full of zest for social gatherings, tripping her way from house to lighted house, chattering and merry, fond of throngs and eager for amusement. But my mother lived almost like a recluse. She enjoyed people when they came to her, but she seldom sought them in return. More and more, as the years passed, she willingly subdued and straitened her life. She renounced without regret the world outside the four walls of her old house, and spoke but little of the earlier years when she had known it. Only sometimes when, in spite of her seclusion, all that was mean and narrow in a small town manifested itself too outrageously, she would turn back to her memories of a freer atmosphere, particularly New York, and she would say with quiet bitterness:

"I'd rather be a lamppost on Vesey Street than the whole city of Norwich, Connecticut."

Outside of the quiet, domestic routine of her home, there was but one weekly event for which she waited and prepared. That was the morning service every Sunday in the Episcopal church on Washington Street. The church stood on a sloping bank beside the Yantic River, a mellow, ivied stone building quite different from the austere white meetinghouse of her childhood on the Norwich Town Green. The interior was hushed and shadowy, the decorations simple and dignified, and the reflections from the stained-glass windows fell across the stone aisles and the dark wood like some rich, translucent fabric. She liked to go early and have a few minutes to kneel for prayer, and then to sit, quietly receptive, looking up into the chancel, withdrawn more and more into herself, until the organ's dreamy preamble died away into the first firm chords of the opening hymn and the clear voices of the choir, as they started up the aisle, brought her to her feet, her hymnal in her hand. But my mother seldom sang. The light, sweet singing voice that had been Mary Hoyt's remained silent while she waited, almost breathlessly expectant, for that instant when the small, robed boy at the head of the procession passed her, carrying high in his conscientious hands the shining symbol of the cross. You could not stand beside her then and not know that she nourished in her heart some purifying flame that would be unbearable, or even impossible, to most women. Often there would be tears against her veil.

Between my mother and the lovely gesture of humility and adoration that she always made when that cross passed her in the church and the little girl Mary, so passionately shaken at the revival meeting years before, stretched a long way. But she had taken it with steadfast feet, and she followed it to the end.

CHAPTER XIV

EXPEDITIONS

THE Sunday atmosphere in our house was serene, but never lugubrious. Somehow fishballs for breakfast started the day with an air of festival that if not religious could hardly be called spiritually harmful. There have always been two devoutly reiterated creeds in regard to this universal New England breakfast, one upholding the merits of the flatter, harder fish*cakes,* the other maintaining the superior qualities of the rounder, softer, and browner fish-*balls*. In our family, we placed our hopes of salvation on the latter variety, with its shapelier appearance and its more delicate flavor. Plentifully heaped upon a broad blue platter, they would be brought in to us still sizzling from the pot of deep fat, and we could scarcely wait to break their tender golden crusts covered with tiny bristles in order to taste the creamy mixture within. My father served them, looking very elegant dressed for church in his cutaway coat and striped trousers, the generous knot of his necktie held by an owl's-head pin. We all ate a great deal, which produced the most amiable mood possible in which to say prayers and receive a blessing.

Going to the Sunday-morning service and returning seemed something in the nature of an expedition, for the church was two miles away, quite close to the city. We no longer had our own horse, Charlie, but Abner Bellows, from a Norwich livery stable, drove us back and forth. Abner dabbled in livery-stable keeping only in the most dilettante fashion. His profession was fishing, and he knew intimately all the branches of it possible to be practiced around Norwich, whether it meant dangling a line off the docks into the Thames, or trolling for pickerel from the stern of a rowboat on Gardiner's Lake, or best of all, wading the rainy brooks in spring casting for trout. Sunday-morning sermons and prayers, the church bells tolling faintly through the soft air, the smells of greening meadows and lawns and also of a not too immaculately kept harness, all remain inextricably mingled in my mind with conversations about fishing.

Often as we trotted home Abner and my father made definite plans, and perhaps during the following week my father took a holiday from the bank, and in company with Abner and his horses, as well as Sam and some of his friends, would start at dawn, their hopes always high for the best catch of any year on record. My mother always rose to pack a lunch for them and to give them a hearty breakfast, which they all ate around the big kitchen table. Occasionally one of the boys ran to look out of the window at the brightening sky, though cloudy weather never disheartened them, for trout were supposed to bite better on a showery day. They drove out most often to Blue Blinds, the farm of the Josiah Baxter who brought us butter, and sometimes a side of native beef, or now and then pigs' feet —"trotters," as he called them in his prim way. When he delivered the butter to my mother, he would say:

"Next week I shall be killing some of my pigs. Would you care for some trotters?"

We always cared for them and they would come, having been cleaned and scrubbed by old Mrs. Baxter until it seemed that they must have belonged to very fastidious porkers who picked their way around only the daintiest of troughs. Saturday night, beside a pot of baked beans and a plate of sliced brown bread, we would behold them on the supper table waiting for us. The meat on them was meager but deliciously tender, and made a good excuse for helping ourselves generously to caper sauce or homemade pickles.

The Josiah Baxter of this time was the son of that earlier Josiah who used to stop for a word with my grandmother in the kitchen. This Josiah remained a bachelor until he was middle-aged, with his aged but unsurrendering mother, running the farm according to all the Baxter traditions. At his mother's funeral, which eventually did take place, he met a kinswoman whom he fancied enough to marry, and it was a great relief to me when I learned that there had been born Josiah Baxter the Third.

"Oh, I'm so glad Mr. Josiah Baxter has a son!" I exclaimed, "for if he hadn't had, who on earth would bring *me* butter when I grow up?"

"Who indeed?" answered my mother, laughing.

The Hale and Baxter families not only had this inherited friendship of several generations, but between them also existed the happiest kind of method for eliminating material waste. For if Mr. Baxter brought us broilers or bacon or those trotters, he also carried away to his farm the rich and overflowing leavings from our table, which in turn provided feed for his pigs and his chickens, so that in the end the whole matter resolved itself into a shining circle of supply and demand.

The Baxter household included no fisherman, though Ephraim Averill, the hired man, was something of a hunter. He had a friendly but rather disdainful interest in how many fish Abner and the Hales took home in the damp moss at the bottoms of the wicker baskets, but for the most part such a sight only excited him to somewhat reticent stories of his own adventures with his gun. Ephraim was a huge, ungainly man who looked utterly incapable of any sentimentality, but he gave himself away by telling of the doe that he came upon in the birch wood one October afternoon. She had not bounded instantly away as he expected she would, but stood regarding him sadly, standing her ground between the silvery trees even as he walked closer and closer through the fallen yellow leaves. And when he lifted his gun to his shoulder, squinting at her down the shining barrel, still she did not stir. Perhaps if Ephraim had tried to shoot her with his eyes shut, she might have gone down under his shot. At least he would never have had to confess that he did not fire at all.

"I jes' couldn't do it," he confided to my father with a shamed grin and a slowly reddening face. "She looked so durn purty."

Drives into the country were, after all, minor expeditions in comparison with the times when we took the train. This did not happen often enough to dull the edge of our enjoyment, even though the destination might be only Glastonbury and the purpose a family funeral in my father's old home there. Since we were the children of the youngest Hale, it always seemed to be death rather than any gay event that drew us into a gathering of the clan.

Aunt Sophia had lived many years alone in the house after my grandfather's death and my father's marriage. Then she was joined by Aunt Lucy Pettigrew and her two children, Walter and Agatha, who were just enough older than Ned and myself to be somewhat contemptuous of our society. An additional reason for their sense of superiority was the fact that their father had been a clergyman from Alabama, and so they boasted a Southern as well as a New England descent. They clung to their Alabaman accent with an almost fanatical tenacity, and Walter fought the Civil War all over again with Ned, more bitterly than ever, out on the side lawn under the elm trees.

Walter always reminded me somewhat of that perplexing apple tree in our own front yard in Norwich Town, the result of Grandfather Hoyt's amateur attempts at grafting; it bore two kinds of apples, neither of them edible. While Walter was in Glastonbury he was savagely a Southerner, but Ned and I were always sure that earlier in Alabama he had been just as aggressively a Yankee.

It would not have been possible to imagine Aunt Sophia living in any other house than the one in Glastonbury. In the reticence and the integrity of her character, the nobility of her bearing, the exquisite austerity of her person and dress, she personified the Hale tradition. But aside from that impression which she gave of being the saintly custodian of both the past and the present, she had a very real hold on the ancestral walls that set her apart from others in the family and which established her right to live and die there in a way that nobody else could claim.

In order to honor his son in the usual Hale way and at the same time to provide shelter for his spinster daughter, the terms of Thaddeus's will had been somewhat singular. He left the property and the house "to my son, John, with the exception of the Southwest bedroom, and access to and from, which I bequeath to my daughter, Sophia." She also received a certain specified corner of the barn, this too with access to and from, in which to keep her cow Marigold. My father accepted these stipulations with his gentle good humor, but also with a feeling of helpless bewilderment. They did not exactly render the homestead possible or comfortable for his own family, when he finally acquired one. Nevertheless, neither Sophia nor his other sisters ever quite forgave him for choosing to live in Norwich Town, nor for taking there some of the Hale possessions from the

Glastonbury rooftree. It was the first time in the long generations that the surviving male had deserted his inheritance, and it seemed not only a blasphemy, but somehow prophetic of the end.

Aunt Sophia had been "stone-deaf" for years and could only hear with the aid of a trumpet attached to a long tube, the end of which she placed in her ear. When you spoke into the trumpet, she listened very attentively, her long, mild face very serious under its smooth roll of white hair, her light-blue eyes half-closed. You waited for an instant after speaking, watching her anxiously. Then it seemed as if your words finally reached her, for she would smile slowly her grave, very sweet smile; her eyes would open full of light, often of amusement, and she would reply in her deep, hollow voice. She was exceedingly tall and large, and her dresses were always made of some uncompromising material like black mohair, the waist a severe sort of bodice with sleeves rather full at the top, and the collar held by a silver brooch edged with pearls, in which a strand of someone's hair had been arranged in three stiff little curving sprays.

There was a gentle uncanniness about Aunt Sophia as she moved among us, for the most part like someone in a very remote dream, but occasionally, and in a startling way, advancing into a conversation with a word or a sentence just appropriate enough to make you wonder if possibly she did hear after all. Engulfed in a profound silence herself, she had a trick of timing those lesser silences which fall on a group of talkers, and into that pause, like a stone into a well, her voice would quietly and deeply drop.

"I can't hear a thing," she would say, and we would all laugh—but just a trifle uneasily.

"Dear Sophia," Aunt Lucy said sometimes in a rather patronizing way. "She lives in the past."

But Sophia lived rather just across the threshold of Time itself, in some room especially reserved for her, and decidedly with "access to and from."

Deafness was a Hale infirmity, a kind of final seal set on the lineage, so that an aging member of the family who did not strain toward a speaker, cupping an ear with a blue-veined hand, was not considered quite authentic. Another kinswoman thus marked as the genuine article was Cousin Martha, whom we saw only once or twice because she lived in England. Her clothes had the same sobriety of material as my aunts', but their fashion seemed a little worldlier, just as the arrangement of her gray hair, which swept up on the forehead from "a widow's peak," had a more studied and less provincial air. She too used a trumpet, but it was a small, elegant affair, which she had bought in London at the same shop where Queen Victoria had bought hers.

The male figures who lingered at the edges of these family groupings were either elderly, drooping, and a little vague, or tall young men so fiercely shy that they blushed scarlet up to the roots of their blond hair if called upon to speak out plainly before the assembled company. They clustered together murmuring local politics or listening to the more voluble women, and when Aunt Lucy brought in sherry and thin slices of her plain, substantial, unfrosted cake, they partook of both with quiet appreciation, but without gaiety or vulgar gusto. They were the husbands and sons of our aunts, as well as members of other families still living in the neighborhood and connected with us by marriages in previous generations. The only ones present actually bearing the name of Hale would be Aunt Sophia, my father, and ourselves, his children. Those others were after all only lesser royalties.

Sam, Ned, and I were subjected to a good deal of inspection on these visitations. Standing very much awed within a circle of our tall kin, broodingly attentive above us, we would hear them say in low tones, "So these are John's children." It was stated a little sadly, not exactly in a voice of complete disappointment, but one nevertheless in which there seemed to sound some shade of melancholy apprehension.

I never found time to explore the Glastonbury house and its surroundings as much as I wanted. People were always interrupting my game of trying to imagine my father as little John Hale, for I was never left alone as I was in Norwich Town, and he himself while with Aunt Sophia and Aunt Lucy had no free moments to lead me down his old bypaths or to show me his favorite fields. Though both sisters were older than he—they often spoke of him as "the baby brother"—they made no decisions, even the smallest, for themselves, but waited always for his final, masculine word of agreement or dismissal.

I had to be patient until Aunt Sophia came down to Norwich Town to visit us. She taught me to knit small oblong facecloths of fine white cotton, and while our ivory needles clicked together—hers very swiftly, mine slowly and in fumbling fingers—she would now and again break her serene silence with some gravely told tale of my father's people. Listening to her was a good deal like listening to an oracle, for her deafness protected her from interruptions, either accidental or intentional. But after I discovered that she nearly always anticipated my questions, I learned to knit away very quietly sitting at her knee, only now and then glancing up at her face, which was as still as one carved out of white stone and from which the voice came rather boomingly, almost as if she spoke to me from an underground cave.

Her girlhood and my father's childhood had been made tragic by the Civil War. Naturally she never told me of her soldier-lover, lost on some battlefield, but I heard often of the three tall young uncles that I would never know, her brothers Thomas, David, and Paul. Thomas and David had both been killed, but Paul survived and came home to Glastonbury, a restless, brooding, melancholy young hero of twenty-three. Somehow he had got it into his head that Connecticut and the Hale inheritance were not for him. Amazingly enough, he wanted to go to Paris and study to be a painter. To his father Thaddeus, already grief-stricken by the loss of his two eldest sons, such an ambition seemed worse than death. They fought it out—the powerful old man with his pride of blood and of long-established position in the community and the passionate young one bent on his own individual vision. It ended finally in the bitterest kind of quarrel, and Paul walked out of his father's study into the wide fields behind the house and shot himself with his army revolver. So Thaddeus saw the end of his three grown sons, all within the space of a few years. There remained to him, for the fulfillment of his hopes, only the one little boy, John.

"Poor Paul, poor Paul," Aunt Sophia would mourn, partly to me but mostly to herself. "He was the handsomest man I ever saw—stood six feet three in his stocking feet. But they were all fine young men. Thomas, who grieved your grandfather so by eloping with that girl from the village. And David—he did so splendidly in the navy; your grandfather was so proud of him. And Paul, poor Paul. Yes, they were all fine young men."

Of my father as a fine young man, Aunt Sophia really knew but little. From the age of nine he had been sent away to school and then to Harvard. She had not lived so close to him as to the others. But she told me one story of his childhood that I found it difficult to regard as other than a special and personal kind of legend. Once when Thaddeus had gone to Washington to visit a kinsman who was in Lincoln's Cabinet, he had taken his small son with him. Mr. Lincoln had patted him on the head, and told him to be a good boy.

"Oh, what did Mr. Lincoln look like?" I asked my father breathlessly, thinking of the picture in my history book—that sad, homely man in the old-fashioned clothes. My father smiled, and said:

"I only remember that when I looked up to see his face I had to look a long, long way."

Thaddeus spared himself no effort or expense to prepare this last boy of his for the life of a Connecticut country gentleman who must keep a firm hand on the affairs of his town, both political and social, and breed strong children as he himself had done. It was fortunate that he died before my father's marriage, and that he never had to face his own final desolation, deserted by a living son who gave his allegiance to his wife's birthplace rather than his own. For if that had not seemed like a cup running over with sorrow, the final drop to embitter it would have been the sight of his son's eldest son—the frail, deformed Sam.

If my father regretted having turned his back on his inheritance, he never said so, at least to us, nor to anyone else so far as we knew. He seemed as much a part of Norwich Town as my mother, and after all the life there was much the same as in Glastonbury, except that every New England town considers a man a stranger unless he has been born within its boundaries. My father knew this, and showed that he accepted it by keeping more and more to himself, making no new close friends, and gradually losing touch with the classmates of his youth, who were widely scattered and most of them far more prosperous than he.

But he possessed one resource against loneliness that my mother lacked—the world of books. Always a student and a reader, he continued not only to store his own mind but to share its delights with his children. Ned and I would clamber up onto the wide arms of his chair, particularly Sunday evenings, begging him to read aloud to us. He was never reluctant, and better still, never tiresomely and solemnly anxious to instruct us. We could have anything we wanted from W. W. Jacobs's stories in the *Strand Magazine* to *Treasure Island,* or narrative verse like "The Dream of Eugene Aram" or "Jim Bludso of the Prairie Belle." Poe was one of his favorite poets, and he hardly glanced at the pages for "Annabel Lee" or "The Raven." But such melancholy magic eluded Ned and myself. We preferred to be drowned in the tumultuous rhyming of "How the Cataract Came Down at Lodore," which always sent us to bed still gasping and gurgling.

Moreover, whether we were puzzled or merely lazy, we could always get help from him in our lessons. He could supply a translation of Latin or French, or the solution of a knotty problem in arithmetic, without the least effort and apparently with considerable entertainment to himself. But he soared highest of all in our estimation on the evening when Ned burst forth with the grievous complaint that he must take an original poem to his English class on the following day, and that he had no idea how to go about so disheartening a task. My father looked slightly astonished, not that such an assignment had been given, but that any son of his should be defeated by the mere thought of its accomplishment. He stared for a short time into the darting flames on the hearth and then, with one of the neatly sharpened pencils that he always carried in his breast pocket, he slowly wrote down three verses on the back of an envelope.

We could not believe that he himself had written a poem, and when he read it out in his gentle voice even my mother listened with us, fascinated. It was a song about pussy willows in the early spring, comparing them to tiny gray squirrels running up bare branches to snatch the silver nuts of the raindrops. Ned studied it incredulously for a while, then folded up the envelope and snapped it shut into the pages of his book, yawning with relief. My mother smiled and went back to her mending, but I sat for a long time with my chin in my hands, my eyes still fixed on my father's face while he went on reading his book as if nothing had happened. I kept thinking to myself:

"He just sat there and made that up in his own head. Why, he can do anything! My father can do anything."

CHAPTER XV

HOLIDAYS

LATE in May, when the air is heavy with the scents of blossoming syringa and white lilacs, there is a certain kind of misty morning that always brings faintly the roll of drums and the sound of men marching. Decoration Day often began with that overcast sky, which added just enough dampness to the dreamy warmth of the ending spring season to make it sticky and a little uncomfortable.

All through the morning people went to the cemetery bearing their wreaths and nosegays to lay on the soldiers' graves. Even those who had no soldiers, but only graves, went too, stripping their gardens of pansies and late tulips, pulling down the last of the pink-flowering apple boughs from the orchards, and going far afield for the wilder blossoms of fen and lane.

Among these faithful mourners who passed our house every year on that May morning was Sarah Stone the seamstress, whose tiny house stood in Mediterranean Lane up on a hillside behind the Green. With her basket of flowers in one hand and her umbrella in the other—since the forenoon threatened to be showery—she went hurrying down the River Road, a small meek figure, her spectacled face thrust slightly forward under its tidy black hat. She was going to decorate her sister Rose's grave.

Rose had spent many years lying on a sofa in the little sunny kitchen while Sarah sat beside her busy with her needlework, which was their only means of support. The two sisters had no knowledge of life outside the small, mighty events in their garden, their lane, and the cliff of rocks that soared up at the back of their house under its tall, somber pine tree. Just once, in the days before Rose's cough had made her too weak even to step alone, some kind person had taken them on a long drive, away over the hills beyond Yantic to Bozrahville, across to the Boggytown Ledges and home by Lover's Lane and Wawecus Woods. They hardly ate or slept that night for thinking of the distances they had covered.

"Why, Rose," said Sarah, her little chin trembling with excitement, "I cannot *bear* to consider the size of the whole world!"

But if Sarah lacked knowledge of her own planet, she atoned for it by an intimate comprehension of worlds within that world. In those ignored, infinitesimal nations underfoot and close at hand but almost invisible except to curious and loving eyes, she was a lifelong traveler of patience and experience. It was she who first startled me one afternoon—while I stood being measured for a dimity dress—by telling me that ants kept cows.

All through the winter she and Rose tended a little row of plants beside the sunny window whose small panes rattled so fiercely when the wind swept up the lane. And in the spring, Rose, her eyes a little starrier each year, her cheeks a little more sunken, from her sofa stared out patiently at the gray cliff, watching the melting snows as they ran down in silver rivulets, waiting for the first tufts of green to sprout in the crevices of the rocks, and later, for the red-and-yellow columbine that she loved so much to hang its fragile flowers along the mossy ledges. So Rose too on Decoration Day always had her sprig of blossoms from her own garden on Mediterranean Lane.

In the afternoon there was a parade that started from Franklin Square in the city of Norwich and marched up Broadway to the Soldier's Monument in the Park, where everyone sat on benches, eating peanuts and drinking root beer out of bottles and listening to the speeches and the music. Then the parade fell into line again on the other side of the Park to march back to the Square down Washington Street.

The figure of the Soldier, homely and more than life-size, in a slouchy cap and baggy trousers, stood leaning on his musket, his face with its blank eyes and drooping mustache staring somberly into the tops of the elms at the far end of the green, triangular Park. Beneath him, cut into the slab of stone, were the names of the battles—Gettysburg, Bull Run, Seven Oaks, The Wilderness, Antietam. Around his clumsy feet were gathered on a wooden platform the city fathers, the speechmakers; and in front of them in the first rows of benches sat the old men in their worn blue uniforms, all with gray or white hair, some very frail, and now and then one leaning far forward, his hand cupping his ear, as the oratory began and almost endlessly, it seemed, continued.

With other children I tried to wriggle in through the indifferent, murmurous throngs, and stand as close as I could to those bundles of weathered clothes which suggested, in some way, the portrait of my Uncle Philip at home. Only Uncle Philip was young. His face was fair and candid, with unlined eyes and a beardless chin. And strangely too, some of these old men dressed like him had faces that were familiar to me, faces that I often saw in the streets or the stores in Norwich—Mr. Curtis the druggist, Elijah T. Porter who worked in the stationery shop, and Mr. Howland—the General, my mother always called him—who lived just below us on the River Road in a house where a tree grew straight up through the veranda. Elijah T. Porter had a wound that never healed, so everyone said, yet he often waited on me when I went into his store to buy my pads and pencils, a thin, stooping man with side whiskers and a kind smile who always wore a skullcap of black on his bald head.

There they all were on Decoration Day, somehow reminiscent of Uncle Philip but at the same time too faded and musty to bear any real relation to him as they sat patiently under the Mayor's jerky gestures and the speeches from the guest politicians. When the ceremonies ended with a flourish and the band burst forth, the spectators rose and started streaming across the lawn toward home. The Park was littered with peanut shells and papers, and on the porches of the big houses under the elms around the Park, the prosperous citizens leaned forward in their rockers to watch the last of the parade as it vanished down Washington Street. The Mayor and his visitors rolled along majestically in their carriages, the militia strode manfully away, and the leader of the band twirled his stick with nonchalance and skill. Warm and bright at last, the late afternoon sun struck through the mist just in time to fall with a tender radiance that was also cruelly revealing across the veterans, their steps so conscientiously brisk behind the limp folds of their sad old flags.

Decoration Day was a solemn holiday in which both the city of Norwich and Norwich Town, as well as the near-by villages, took part. On the Fourth of July they once more drew apart to commemorate history, each in its own way. Neither the fashionable Park nor the business section at Franklin Square would have tolerated the kind of celebration that continued all night before the Fourth on the Norwich Town Green. The city had a police force, but Norwich Town had only Bill Tompkins, the one-eyed sheriff. The first three days of July Bill put on a fine show of roaring, ranting, and threatening. He rattled his handcuffs ominously and talked about "bein' law-abidin' " and how he would have all offenders "baound over t' the Superior Court." But his words were not taken seriously, and they only added to the delight or the discomfort of anticipation—according to age, disposition, and condition of health—of all the neighborhood.

No matter how much Bill rolled his one burning eye, nor how carefully Mr. Littlefield, the earnest sexton of the meetinghouse, hid his keys, some sly boy always found his way up into the tower and gave the poor old bell the only joyous release in its whole dolorously sacred career. Its drunken tongue started caroling on the stroke of midnight, punctuated by blasts of dynamite set off on a blacksmith's anvil that other boys had dragged to the center of the Green. These explosions, the superb sound of ringing iron, and the indecent clamor of the bell made the night miserable for the minister, the deacons, and the various old ladies—like Aunty Richards—who lived around the Green. This continued until dawn, and the rest of the day, with its puny poppings of pistols and firecrackers and its twilight starred with rockets, suffered in comparison.

There was one traditional ceremony observed in all Norwich—both city and town—which seemed to be entirely local, though it was known in other Connecticut towns during the eighteenth century. On Thanksgiving evening barrels that had been begged, borrowed, or otherwise acquired were rolled to vacant lots, strung up on long poles, and burned. Touched off at night, the roaring flames drawn up through and around them, they made very spectacular bonfires, and wherever you might be, you could see these tall red streamers rising from the fields and hillsides all around the town. Some people thought this was the continuation of a custom originally practiced on Guy Fawkes Day, when an effigy of the Pope was always burned. During the Revolution Washington issued an order to his soldiers forbidding such a demonstration because of the French allies, who were Roman Catholics. Later it was resumed for a while, using Benedict Arnold as the symbolic victim. Apparently the traitor was not so much fun as the Pope, for he gradually disappeared altogether; but the bonfires remained—at least in Norwich on Thanksgiving Day.

Stringing the barrels in the morning gave my father not only a chance to be with Ned and his friend Beany and some of the other boys, but it also provided an excellent way—so he thought—to work up an appetite for Thanksgiving dinner, which we always had early in the afternoon. When it was time to light our fire, his presence also reassured Mr. Burrill the farmer, who allowed us to use one of his lots across the river. This was not close enough to any house to be dangerous, but at their height the flames often gleamed back from the near-by stream, and even glowed faintly in the front panes of our house across the meadows.

When everything had smoldered down to embers and the piercing November cold began to strike through us, we turned and trooped home over the iron bridge, looking back every now and then to see if any sparks were still rising rosily through the dark. We always ended the day in the kitchen, where my father put on a big apron and popped corn for us. We sat together around the table with its red cloth, and passed the big yellow mixing-bowl from one to another, rapidly and hungrily reducing its mound of fluffy white kernels to a few black seeds in the buttery bottom of the bowl.

Another holiday that ended for us with a party in the

kitchen was Nutting Day. It came in October; the schools closed, and the children went off to their favorite—and often secret—places on a hunt for chestnuts. It was likely to be an Indian-summer day, with no wind and a warm sun that sent bright shafts through the thinning bronze and golden boughs in the woods. Already so many leaves lay on the ground that, searching through them, our hands would strike a prickly burr so hard that it hurt. Sometimes we had to pound the burrs apart on the stone wall, but when we were lucky, they lay already split open on the grass, and luckiest of all, occasionally we found one whose silky gray hollow held four nuts, fitted there exactly, something like a four-leaf clover.

The best trees were big and stately, and stood at the roadside or the edge of a wood. Scuffing around under the wide branches, we filled our pockets, sometimes stopping to eat, cracking the thin shells with our teeth. If we were too hasty, and did not first examine the nut for any tell-tale tiny black hole, we would bite square into the plump white body of a worm. But even so, we merely made a face, spat out the whole affair, and the next instant picked up another nut and began again, this time more observantly. Raw chestnuts eaten under the tree were hard, sweet, and ivory-white. Roasted at home, the shells cracked open, the meat became softer and mealier, and with the additional flavor conferred by fire we could almost fancy ourselves feasting on elfin potatoes.

Remembering the richly sensuous adventure of a country childhood, one finds it difficult to tell which of the five gateways to the awakening spirit swung the widest, and which welcomed in the loveliest and the most exotic strangers. If the tongue's tip was a dangerous entrance, for that very reason it was exciting, and after it had learned, painfully, to refuse iron in winter, or a lick from a workingman's quid, it could find exquisite pleasure in such sweets as a snowflake caught in flight, or one minute square floret from a lilac spray, pressed against the roof of the mouth for the sake of its drop of honey.

Then, always and forever, there was salt. But that was one cup which I did not need to tilt alone in solitary delight. An annual taste of salt on all the Haleses' tongues was as necessary as daily food. This pleasant craving drove us no farther away from our gentle hills than to the near-by Rhode Island coast, but because of the circuitous routes of the railroads as well as the wait in New London between trains, and then at the end a long drive out of the town of Westerly, the trip occupied the better part of a day.

Our preparations for this month of salt were as elaborate as though for a tour in Europe, and there was as much discussion about the house—how best to close it and leave it "alone" for those four weeks, as if indeed it had been a living and breathing personality. Seen from the train windows as at last we steamed away down the tracks past that gap in the woods, across the river and the meadows, the house looked whiter than ever, like a face suddenly overspread with the pallor of one left behind, grieving and desolate. That brief, flying glimpse was a piercing one, but soon forgotten in the later excitements of the day.

The drive from Westerly out to Weekapaug Beach, where we stayed, led through the outskirts of the town and then over roads growing sandier and lonelier, the lush green of the urban foliage changing to low pines and straggling wild-rose bushes. At the top of a long, hot, treeless incline, where the horses moved at a leisurely pace infuriating to our impatience, we would see for the first time, far down and across the marshes, with the brown line of dunes at the right and the cluster of gray shacks and cottages at the left, the wide glitter of the ocean. At that moment we always leaned forward in our seats, breathing deeply, and crying out:

"Oh, smell it, smell it! Oh, now you can smell the salt!"

Cuttingly across the hot, spicy fragrances of bayberry and sweet fern would blow that bitter, cool, and infinitely refreshing draught. And as we quickened our pace down the white road between the barren but beautiful wastes that stretched far away on either side, soaked in the white sunlight, we would hear, louder and louder, the breathtaking sound of the surf on the shore.

Long years before, my mother had said to my father:

"I wish we could find some place where the last thing I hear at night, and the first in the morning, is the sound of waves on a beach."

Here she had her wish, and as soon as she stepped out of the carriage she would walk—almost run—across to the sand and down to the very edge of the bubbling water.

The Inn stood up, bleak and unadorned, a shingled building on a strip of land between the ocean and a long salt pond where we could dawdle about in rowboats and canoes, or sail up and down through the breezy afternoons, with my father at the tiller of a small sturdy catboat.

People came to the Inn and the cottages around it from many other localities besides Connecticut. It elated me to discover one little girl who lived so far away as Cleveland, Ohio. Such a real Westerner as that, I thought, must prove different from any children I had ever known in Norwich, where even visitors from Albany were eyed warily and spoken of as Albanians. But she was depressingly like myself, I found, and had nothing to tell of life in Cleveland that could satisfy my hopes of some free and superb state of savagery.

On the ocean side of the Inn, the beach curved away in a white crescent to the lifesaving station at Quonochontaug. In the opposite direction, it rose into a point of tumbled rocks where the tons of water struck and broke thunderously, scattering spray across the barnacles and clinging seaweed, receding with the murmur of a thousand indistinct voices as the foam bubbled back hissing over the smooth white pebbles. The pools among the rocks were like clear glass spread above enchanting little seascapes, over which I would bend staring into the waving pink and brown fronds, or watch for starfish or the small, sidling crabs.

Swimming in that surf was boisterous and rough. Often I left it, panting, to lie stretched out in the sand, fiery hot against my dripping length. The grains ran in a glistening stream through my fingers, and so scared the tiny white-shelled sandfleas with their popping silvery eyes that they vanished scrambling into their shallow burrows.

On clear days—and always a sure sign of stormy weather the next day—far across the water rose the dark-blue line of Block Island, where my father had courted my mother. Ships passed, hardly moving and yet seemingly soon gone, showing up at night only as a cluster of little sparkles.

Drenched in all that dazzling light, the only green the metallic luster of the sparse eelgrass rattling in the breeze, the seasons were forgotten. Even the dusty miller, straggling down the dunes, had leafage almost as colorless as the sand. Returning home the first of September, our sun-dazzled eyes that had squinted so long into all that brilliance opened wide into the mellow light falling across the richness of the shadowy green lawn. Ned and I always ran out to the grape arbor, where the purple grapes hung ripe and rounded. The phlox around the summerhouse was bending under its weight of white flowers, and along the uncut edges of the meadows by the river the goldenrod and the asters stood tall and full of bloom. We heard the bell in the public school up on the Green clanking in the scholars, as it had so long ago in spring. Soon Miss Lucas too, in our own school, would be waiting for us with sharpened pencil and opened book. Then the summer and the long holidays would be really over.

Down the street would come the twinkling buggy and the graceful horse of Dr. Burton Palmer. He would see us standing by the grape arbor, and lean forward to wave and call a welcome home.

"Ah, there! How are you?"

How resplendent he looked in his white summer suit, with red socks, a red necktie, and a rose to match them in his buttonhole.

And, oh, how very strange it seemed that house and

river and meadow were all here to receive us, apparently untouched by our absence! We had been gone a whole month! We, the Hales, had been away! And yet the town and its events, the summer and its harvest, had been continuing as usual, and obviously quite as well, without us.

CHAPTER XVI

LESSONS

ONE of my earliest tutors in American history was a French soldier who came to this country during the Revolution and died on the Norwich Town Green, where with others of his countrymen he had been encamped. This man and nineteen of his companions were buried on a deeply shaded hillside that sloped back from the walled garden behind our house. In one of the early years of the present century the D.A.R. had gathered up all that could be found of the scattered skeletons of these exiles, and they were put in one grave under a suitable memorial stone. But for a few days the bones lay uncovered in a little heap. One noontime when the gravediggers were away, I wandered up the steps from our garden into the lane that led on toward the old burying-ground. I saw that small heap gleaming in the grass and stood for a moment staring at it. Then I knelt down beside the bones and took a skull into my hands.

No doubt I should have been deeply moved—terrified even—by this stark introduction to death and to the history of all humanity. Instead, I was excited because I was looking at a Frenchman out of the legend of my own land. I did not then know any French people, and they seemed quite as foreign as angels. I felt that the material of which they were made must be somehow significantly different from others—certainly from that of myself.

Like most children, I was an accomplished thief, and it may well have entered my head to slide that polished treasure into my blouse, where I had so often harbored such lesser objects as apples, pears, and at Hallowe'en even small pumpkins. It is one more honor to be accorded the unknown Frenchman that he commanded my respect as well as my curiosity. Gently I laid the skull down again among the other fragments. For some time I knelt there, like an infant female Hamlet, lost in meditation, and never after did certain pages in my history book seem quite so much like empty print. If I could not say that I had seen Lafayette in the flesh, at least I could always remember how I, a small twentieth-century American, had touched alone by myself this fugitive keepsake from eighteenth-century France.

The only person who really understood the way I felt about this experience was Miss Cynthia Lucas. Miss Cynthia and her sister, Miss Arabella, were my two teachers, who, as they themselves would have stated it, "conducted a school" on North Washington Street not far from the Park. It was the only private establishment of its kind in the town, and its eighteen or twenty scholars, including my brother Ned and myself, were children from that elect circle known as "the nicest families."

These two maiden ladies were never spoken of in the plural as the Lucases, but always, with a chuckle, as the Lucae. They were both very proud of their black eyes, which they said were rare in New England and a mark of their French ancestry. Sometimes Miss Cynthia told us about her Huguenot forebears and their bitter persecutions in France. One story had come down in her household, passed on from one generation to the other, of the way their Bible had been hidden from the gendarmes by being strapped open under a chair. The instant that the officers appeared, the chair was put in position and one of the family—probably a woman with spreading skirts—sat in it until the inspection of the house was over.

Miss Cynthia, the elder sister, must have been the original pattern from which all New England school-teachers were cut. She was rather tall, with white hair smoothly parted and drawn back over her ears into a firm knot at the back of her head. She wore spectacles, behind which those very dark eyes either beamed or snapped as the occasion or the culprit warranted. She had an erect spare figure, and moved quickly but with dignity. She wore plain dresses, in winter of speckless black, in summer of immaculate white. She kept her handkerchief tucked into her right cuff, and a gold watch in the belt of her waist. Her whole effect was one of uncreasable cleanliness starting from the very center of her spirit.

She was strict, courteous, and grave, always alert for any event and never unappreciative if it happened to prove amusing. She never laughed out loud, but smiling with compressed lips, she would quiver slightly in a controlled manner, and often she would shake her head from side to side, squeezing her eyes up tightly for a second. To recover herself, she always removed her spectacles, drew the handkerchief out of her cuff, polished the spectacles, put them on again, and with her eyes still twinkling, signified by a lifted pencil that we were once more ready to proceed with whatever serious matter had been in hand before the frivolous interruption. In speaking, she pronounced each syllable with meticulous care. For instance, the word pupil was "pew-pill." She had a soft, clear voice, rather low in tone, and she spoke ordinarily quite slowly, but at times when she wished to be emphatic the words came more quickly, though never indistinctly. "Yes, yes, yes, oh, indeed, *yes!*" she would say.

Miss Arabella, the younger sister, was shorter, gentler, and vaguer. She swayed from side to side a little as she fluttered about, and often said, "Dear, dear!" or "My, my!" in a bewildered sort of way. She was nearly always smiling, and when she laughed it sounded like a gay little girl. She wore her gray hair drawn up in a knot on the top of her head and fluffed out slightly at the sides. Her dresses were of colored materials trimmed with little beadings, bows, or frills, and they rustled pleasantly as she moved about. Whenever confronted by any important decision, she always said, "I will consult my sister." We called her Miss Arabella, but Miss Cynthia was always Miss Lucas.

As the school was the Lucases' own home, there was only one room that seemed at all like a formal school. We called it the study hall, and there we had our desks and kept our books. At nine o'clock we all assembled in that room at the ringing of a small silver bell and sat more or less quietly for a prayer and a chapter from the Bible read by Miss Lucas. Most of the classes, however, were held in the dining-room, the parlor, or the library, a small, bright room at the end of a long dark hall. Sometimes between classes one or two of us might be allowed to go upstairs to the Blue Room for a study period. But this was a rare privilege extended only to the trustworthy, and it ceased altogether after Mrs. Johnson came to board with the Lucases.

Mrs. Johnson was the widow of a Senator, and earlier had known years of prosperity in a large Victorian mansion facing the Park. But she ended her days in the Lucas Blue Room. A frail, tiny woman, often wearing a white shawl, she seemed very old to us—older even than Miss Lucas—in the few glimpses that we had of her. She evidently rose late, and only occasionally left her room to creep softly up and down stairs and through the dim hall. Sometimes her curiosity got the better of her discretion and she would peek around the corner of the door of the study hall where some of us were sitting. Then she would make a mischievous face at us, and just once, very daringly, she hissed out, "You little *bugs,* you!" and then instantly vanished up the stairs.

The Blue Room was directly over the study hall, and

one morning as we were studying there we were startled by sounds overhead as if someone were playing leapfrog with terrific energy. We looked up with wide eyes and began to grin and whisper.

"Silence, children, silence!" ordered Miss Lucas from the table by the window, where she sat correcting our papers. "It is nothing—only Mrs. Johnson adjusting her hose."

We were quelled, although the explanation only made us wonder whether that fragile little lady wore stockings of steel, and if she jumped into them from the top of the bureau.

We scholars were the usual blurred, murmurous huddle of any group of children, only now and then by squirms or faint squeals showing signs of our leashed vitality. But once in a while one of us by means of some episode stood out as an individual, as one bubble will break away from clustered foam at a brook's edge and appear clearly for an instant, solitary in its own bobbing liveliness, until shoved back into the mass by the current of the stream.

We all poked a good deal of fun at Willie Burton, the fat boy. Our taunting reached one of its highest points on that spring day at recess when he sat down on a bumblebee and completely demolished it. He had to endure as best he could the sight of the smashed corpse passed from hand to hand with suitable insults by everyone. Nevertheless, he gained some respect from us as a reward for the flash of genius that he showed in giving advice to Allen Rossiter in a moment of dire distress. Allen would never "take a dare," and when challenged to eat some leaves of poison ivy, he had done so, with the inevitable result.

"It itches awful," he kept complaining, writhing over his desk.

"Aw, go home and swallow a lot of toast," said Willie. "That'll scratch it."

The girls all understood each other placidly enough, with the one exception of feverish, witchlike little Estelle Lamb. We were somewhat baffled by her thin wrists clanking with bracelets, and her large eyes that glittered so strangely in the small face framed by its bush of soft hair. Passing between classes, Estelle often contrived a moment of loitering on the small sofa in the dimmest corner of the hall under the staircase, pulling one of the boys down beside her. "Secrets" of some kind were hastily but flamingly divulged by Estelle. The boy would emerge into the light, his hair mussier even than usual, looking sheepish and giggling, and behind him airily stepped Estelle, her face quite demure except for the glint of triumph in her eyes.

Miss Lucas and Miss Arabella, unperturbed by these minor disturbances, moved serenely through their mornings, their quiet voices, assisted by the peremptory but silver-tongued little bell, perfectly competent to command and maintain order.

Miss Lucas taught arithmetic and history, the first with methodical care and patience, but the second with such an air of adoration that it seemed almost religious. She would say of Washington and Major André:

"And the tears simply *streamed* down Washington's face when he signed that death warrant."

There we would sit, spellbound on our straight little

chairs gathered in a circle around her, not only convinced of the tears but also of Miss Lucas's presence at the moment of their streaming. She *must* have met George Washington, we thought. Wasn't she old enough, and didn't she know everything there was to know about him?

Then there was a "history game," which we called among ourselves "swapping dates." One child selected a date from the book and challenged another child to name the event that went with it. If the answer was correct, that child had the next chance to challenge. One morning I was tossed the year 1500 by Peter Hopkins. Peter was a formidable boy behind spectacles, whose erudition was staggering, and a special delight and pride of Miss Lucas's.

But I happened to know that his life was not entirely devoted to the intellect, for I had caught him more than once in the hall with Estelle. Fortified by this knowledge, which gave me, I thought, some right for scorn, I faced him courageously as he sat alert on the edge of his chair, his hands on his knees, an I've-got-her-now expression behind his sparkling glasses. Fifteen hundred, 1500? My whole mind went on a scrambling and frantic hunt, and my body twisted and turned in sympathy. Suddenly, blindingly, after an instant of perfect and agonizing blank, the answer, the complete sentence exactly as it stood in the book, was printed on my inner eye.

"A-a-a-ah!" I gasped, leaping to my feet, my pigtails out straight. I pointed at him derisively. "A-ah-*ha!*" I reiterated with triumphant emphasis. "The Spanish flag, the *Spanish* flag waved over all!"

He crumpled. And I sat down, spreading out my plaid skirts with complacence. Miss Lucas bent forward rigidly, but rocking softly with delight. Off came her spectacles, out came her handkerchief, and it was a full two minutes before the lifted pencil again commanded us to attention. She was something of a feminist, I think, in her own sedate way.

Miss Arabella taught us geography, usually in the dining-room, where we sat at a round table covered with a red-fringed cloth. She seemed a tremulous little figure to deal with such giants as the poles, the continents, and climate, but nevertheless she had her moments of sturdy briskness, and this class was one of them. Also she had her own quaint way of illustrating cold facts with imaginative exhibits. One of these was the Grand Canyon in a bottle. Someone had brought her this souvenir from the Far West, and it had been treasured ever since on the "what-not" in the parlor, together with the curly sea shell, the coral fan from Bermuda, the coffee cup from Turkey, the Indian arrowhead, and the carved sandalwood box. It was an ordinary little glass medicine bottle, but within it, in colored layers, reposed the rainbow soil "just as it looks in the Grand Canyon."

Once, to illustrate an earthquake, she tripped out into the kitchen and came back bearing a loaf of gingerbread that had been baked that morning. There were the cracks, sure enough, in something as dark and crumbly as earth itself. It was near noontime, but after due observation and comment back to the kitchen cupboard went the gingerbread intact, and with watering mouths we bent once more over the red tablecloth. But ever after I felt sure that should the earth open at my feet, up from the abyss would float that rich, delicious fragrance.

To study English—only we called it Language then—we trooped out through the dark hall to the small, bright library at the rear of the house. We sat around a table there too, and it was difficult to concentrate in the spring, because one of the windows framed a view of bright-green marshland, in the foreground a blossoming apple tree with a weatherbeaten wooden bench beneath it. Miss Sterry, a neighbor of the Lucae, taught the class in Language. She was a plump, prim lady with curly dark hair and rather cold, protuberant brown eyes. At one time she had been a missionary to Turkey, and often while we were writing our lesson she would reread letters from some of her Turkish friends. The letter paper was thin and rustling, the pages covered closely with a fine and of course to us indecipherable script. Sometimes she told us a little about the Turks, but she always spoke of them sadly and cryptically, as if they weren't quite people. She only added to my confusion about missionaries, a state no doubt first brought about by a remark of my grandfather's which I often heard repeated at home. Someone had told him that a parson of his acquaintance—a Dr. Gear—had departed for Turkey to be a missionary.

"Fine!" my grandfather had exclaimed. "Fine for Gear—but tough on the Turks!"

We all heard a good deal about Armenians at that time too. We even had one family living in the town, rescued, I suppose, from those luckless Turks. They lived in an old brown house by the side of the road on our way to school. My brother Ned and I always passed it each day, and often Mr. Ambrosian, the father of the family, would be out in the yard chopping wood. He was a ferocious-looking man with a black mustache, and he chopped with resounding vigor. Their place was about the halfway point on our walk home, and often at noon I would be tired and lag, which irritated Ned. So he thought of a brilliant though malevolent scheme to hasten my footsteps.

"You see that man there—that Ar-*meen*-ian—chopping that wood," he would whisper, rolling his eyes in a perfectly solemn face. "Well, that man there is a girl-eater! If you don't hurry up, he'll come out here after you!" I didn't quite believe it—not quite—though the ax, the mustache, and the Armenianism somehow seemed to support the horrid fable. So I would take to my heels.

There was no afternoon session in Miss Lucas's school. I used to wonder how she spent her own afternoons in a house emptied of the morning's bustle—holding ghostly discourse with George Washington, perhaps. As for me, if I chose I could walk up in the lane past my French soldier and on into the old burying-ground. There were no mounds any more in the long grass dappled with the slender gray shadows from the weeping-willow trees. But many of the dark gravestones still rose up among the buttercups and the daisies. Several of them said to me sternly:

As I am now, so you shall be.
Prepare for Death and follow me.

I was never disconcerted. I went on over the little hill into the sun and down to the meadow, where I followed the brook; its tune was livelier and more enticing.

CHAPTER XVII

THE TWO TOWNS

BEHIND the meetinghouse on the Norwich Town Green rose a sharp cliff known as the Meeting House Rocks, green and wooded on its sides, its summit rather bare except for grassy ledges and low-growing, shrubby trees. In the earliest days the first church had been built on the top of this cliff, where the height of the situation was a distinct advantage for the lookout who while others worshiped must watch the meadows and river marshes lying below for any shadowy signs of swiftly running Indians.

There was then no River Road but merely a kind of trail crossing the meadows. It was lonely enough by day, and at night not only lurking Indians and wolves but huge snakes as well had made it dangerous for solitary travelers. Even in my own childhood, I avoided at dusk that section of the road just below our house, before you came to the little cluster of painted buildings—cottages, shanties, and the blacksmith shop—which my grandfather always called Yellowtown. The fields stretched out darkly and limitlessly on either side of the roadway when night fell, and the maple trees on the sidewalk stirred and rustled mysteriously in the shadows overhead. It was a place where I always ran, remembering the Indians, and wondering whether the mist that often lay wanly along the river had anything to do with their restless wraiths.

But nobody watched for Indians from the later meetinghouse, which stood at the foot of Meeting House Rocks. The trolley cars stopped there to take on passengers before going on around the edge of the Green, and it seemed a safe and sociable spot. My mother and I often took the ten-o'clock trolley at that point, going "downtown" on errands or for calls. This particular trolley was the aristocratic one, and on it we nearly always met the same people from Norwich Town.

One little old lady, whose bonnet glistened with black jet and who always in every season carried a palm-leaf fan, told me each time I met her that she had known my English grandmother. The fan had a metal clip at the top, which she held against her teeth to help her hearing. As you replied to her, she peered at you over the fan with beady eyes and a birdlike air. It seemed that she had been one of the little girls who had peeked over the wall at my grandmother in her garden when she first came to Norwich Town, a bride and "a foreigner." Staring up into that moled and mottled face under its fringe of gray hair, I would think, "Oh, so you were one of those, were you?" —my imagination floundering in its attempt to recover from that overgrown ruin some faint outline of the original little girl.

And then Mr. Edgar Mory and his sister Mrs. Lucinda Grace, a widow in a long black veil, would board the trolley, which obligingly stopped just beyond the entrance to their old red house in the hollow. Mr. Mory combined courtliness of manner with a whimsical sense of humor, which always made the gathering on the trolley quite a gay one. His beaked face with its eyes blinking sharply under an assumed slight scowl had somewhat the expression of a benignant owl. On summer mornings, when he bowed and brought his hat down very low before him, and before you, you were likely to find a rose lying within it. I learned to expect this little ceremony—never tactlessly exchanged with the same lady on successive days—but not without anxiety, for his hair was thinning on top, and his roses grew on a thorny bush. It was always with relief that I saw the token delivered, and knew that his head could lie easy, divested of the flowery crown under his hat. As well as courtliness he had kindness, particularly to children. In the fall when they came to gather chestnuts on his hillside above the meadows, they always found hundreds lying ready to their hands in the grass, as though long since burst out of the prickly shells. But he himself had abetted Nature by going to the store for a large extra supply in a paper bag and had scattered them around on the grass so that no one should be disappointed.

Mr. Mory and my mother had both been brought up as Congregationalists, but had acquired through life what they called "a leaning towards the High Church." They liked to discuss this on those morning rides to town, but always in discreetly lowered tones. And if they went so far as to speak favorably even of Catholicism, their heads would bend very close together, and their faces wear an expression of almost joyous guilt.

The really supreme moment on the ten-o'clock trolley arrived when Miss Maria Aspinwall stepped aboard. She took her own good time to do so, though her foot was light and her form virginally slim; and it was noticeable that the respectful elderly conductor did not signal to the motorman to proceed on his way until she had swishingly arranged herself in her seat. Miss Maria wore a modified hoop skirt, which tilted up slightly as she sat down, revealing her stout, homely little shoes. Her hair was cut short like a boy's, and her small round hat was held firmly in place by an elastic at the back of her head. She had a wizened wee face like a crinkled mask, through which you seemed to see a child looking out at you with curiosity and candor. She never gave the impression of being in any way conscious that her singular figure differed from that of everybody else, or disconcerted because somewhere along the years she had fallen out of step with fashion and had never troubled to hurry into line again. Everyone spoke of her, not without affection, as Miss Hoopskirt Aspinwall, and if she knew it, I am sure she didn't care.

This particular trolley seemed to weave its circuitous

way toward Franklin Square with its clamor muffled, and with more than the usual disregard for anything so urgent as a schedule. The passengers were few and demure, and the conductor, a thin man with a drooping mustache and a worn collar scraping his Adam's apple, collected his fares in a manner almost reluctant, not to say deprecatory.

After the car reached the Park with the Soldier's Monument, there were few additions to the group within. Those who lived around the Park and on the two main streets below it for the most part had their own carriages, and drove the remaining mile to the city seated elegantly behind their stolid Irish coachmen, whose jowls seemed to be always nearly the same hue as their plum-colored livery. Every sunny afternoon, too, these carriages, most of them victorias, set forth on their leisurely way toward Norwich Town, and sometimes farther on to Bean Hill and Yantic.

There was one lady in particular, Mrs. Samuel de Trafford Greene, who presented a very rich and refined appearance as she rolled past our house on the River Road, her sleekly groomed black horses prancing along at a dignified pace, the coachman in his correct attitude of stony boredom, holding the whip at an angle, sitting very straight on his high, uncomfortable little seat. Behind him, usually alone on the cushions, was draped Mrs. Greene, dressed in trailing delicate black, and wearing a small toque with a daintily tight-drawn veil. Pinned to her waist she wore a bunch of purple violets, and their scent, no doubt augmented by some exotic perfume, would be wafted through the still golden air as she continued on her regal way along the shady street. Whenever possible, I stood at the front gate to take a look at and have a sniff of this truly august personage. Except for the steady sound of the horses' hoofs on the firm dust of the white road, she passed as silently and as smoothly as a chariot in a dream. It used to seem to me that one could long for nothing lovelier than to be a grown-up lady in a victoria forever riding up and down the highway, alone and serene and smelling of violets, throughout the hours of a hazy summer afternoon.

Like Mrs. Greene, there was a worldliness about all the people in the city of Norwich which those in Norwich Town wholly lacked. Theirs was an ampler life with a richer texture, more like that of other prosperous places anywhere in America at that time, while we in the old shabby, sleepy part of the community still preserved much of the austerity and the innocence that belonged to the earlier centuries and the more provincial ways. Many of those people who lived near and around the Park might have stepped out of the broad gold frames of mellow paintings, like portraits come to life but still not unforgetful of which attitude to take to keep the profile in the softest light or the "limbs" most gracefully revealed. We who still stayed in our smaller, mustier houses so much closer to the woods and lonely country roads were far more naïve. None of us could have suggested a figure taken out of a luxurious picture. But there were some among us who might have walked straight into the verses of an ancient ballad set to plaintive music heard from far away, and have found there a singularly appropriate home.

When I think of Norwich and Norwich Town, I always remember two names and two lives as different and as individual as the two towns themselves, yet both a part, as the towns were also, of the childhood when I ran foot-loose under the sky to see what I could see, or sat sedately beside my gossiping elders, perfectly silent but dreadfully alert.

It was from those overheard, unguarded conversations—long before I saw him—that I gathered my first impressions of Mr. Alexander Navarre. His square white house with the shutters nearly always discreetly closed stood on lower Broadway, one of the most attractive mansions between the Park and the business section of the city. Mr. Navarre, however, seldom occupied it, as he was one of those fortunate expatriates of the late nineteenth century who preferred to cultivate their talents for a dreamy indolence in France rather than to exert themselves in boring activities at home. Two memorable remarks of Mr. Navarre's were either wafted across the intervening seas or else had been dropped inadvertently during some short sojourn in Norwich. The first was a complaint uttered when he had been annoyed at some time by being caught in a coarsely overcrowded atmosphere.

"There are too many people in the world," he announced. "Some of them ought to be destroyed."

On hearing this repeated, my mother laughed and said, "Alexander, of course, would be among those saved."

The other remark was a boast with such implications that the town, being what it was, might have been expected to gasp with horror and scowl with disgust. Instead, knowing its Alexander, it only laughed tolerantly when it learned that he had boasted of his power to seduce "any woman" provided he was given "twenty minutes alone with her."

Whether it was with the idea of accepting this challenge to chastity, or because Mr. Navarre had the reputation of knowing just where and how to divert himself tastefully in Paris (possibly for both reasons), at least it was certain that whenever his townswomen traveled abroad, they invariably sought him out. Mrs. Navarre apparently was a manageable spouse who remained not only obligingly rich and childless, but also in the background, invisible, whenever Alexander sallied forth upon his little escapades. However, she had been known to express herself once and so forcefully that the echoes of her bitter tongue went clear across the Atlantic, and its reverberations continued in Norwich for some time.

Alexander's cousin and onetime playmate Foster had married a charming, mischievous woman from New York. After this Mrs. Foster Navarre became a widow, she too spent much of her time in Europe and she was often in Paris. Driving out one day under the budding springtime trees, she was astonished to catch sight of Alexander standing on one of the little bridges that cross the Seine, kissing Miss Arrietta Barber. Arrietta lived on Washington Street in Norwich, and she had come abroad with her sister Sue on a little trip in pursuit of culture. Giggling with wicked delight, Mrs. Foster Navarre passed on unseen. She could hardly wait until she returned to her hotel, where she sat down immediately and wrote a note to Alexander teasing him about his kiss.

Unfortunately Mrs. Alexander opened the note. No doubt she recognized the handwriting, and as she always suspected villainy whenever Foster's wife appeared, she could not resist reading the contents of the letter. What the good lady said to her Alexander was never published in Norwich, though of course it was imagined with much and pleasurable malice. But soon everyone at home had her opinion in black that fairly quivered across white, not only of Arrietta but also of Mrs. Foster Navarre. As all the principals in this small comedy had friends and relatives in the town, sides were taken and tongues clacked joyously. It even developed, between certain groups, into a feud of considerable entertainment and absurdly long duration. The only commitment on the matter ever made by Alexander himself was the gentlemanly understatement that Mrs. Foster Navarre was "a charming creature, but a trifle indiscreet." But probably Dr. Burton Palmer, who knew and understood them all, got the most satisfactory amusement out of the whole affair.

"Well, well," he remarked with his husky chuckle, "that's a long way to go to kiss a girl from Norwich!"

Eventually all this was carried up to Norwich Town and across our threshold, as across all the others. It added one more dash of richness to the already warmly romantic colors in which we thought of Mr. Navarre as being painted. Yet of course when at last I actually saw him for the first time, he seemed to me, a wide-eyed little girl, quite elderly and brittle to bear the reputation of all that rosy gallantry. Nevertheless, he impressed me during the early days of some summer when for a brief time he came home, and his house with the shutters fastened back appeared to open its eyes and to smile genially at the foliage that cast cool shadows across the wide stones in the sidewalk and the macadam street. He would set forth at his unhurried, almost stately pace, a slim, immaculate gentleman carrying a white umbrella. The waxed ends of his silver mustache stood out stiffy against his florid cheeks, and on the little finger of his right hand—a hand that "had never soiled itself in labor"—gleamed a ruby ornately set in heavy gold. On eleven o'clock of a sunny forenoon, he would be on his way downtown to the bank to cut his coupons.

No, we had nothing anywhere in Norwich Town so scandalously splendid and aglisten as Mr. Alexander Navarre. And it is no doubt curious that my memory should have selected to keep beside his delicate and polished figure that other one of so cracked an earthenware, Jerry, the Blue Bag. Since I saw Mr. Navarre only at long intervals and I came upon Jerry every spring as regularly as I found the patch of violets by the brook, I should know far more about him than I do about Mr. Navarre. But I have much less to tell. He was never heard to speak to any of us, so that it still remains a mystery how we came to know that he was one who had been "crossed in love" in his youth. But he was one of the sure signs of spring, appearing from nobody knew just where, following down from the hills the last clear trickle of the melting snows, crossing the Norwich Town Green, and walking down the middle of the road to vanish at the turn near Yellowtown.

He walked barefoot, carrying a shoe under either arm, and his clothes, including the stuffed bag slung across one shoulder (which gave him the only last name he ever owned), were all of one faded and shabby blue. No matter how the dogs growled or the children snickered and catcalled, he looked straight ahead, intent on some pilgrimage or the desolate retracing of it. Standing on the roadside one day as he slouched along through the drying mud under the boughs blurred with their first faint red and golden leafage, I was close enough to see his eyes. And they too were an old and poverty-stricken blue.

Somehow, in comparison with Jerry, that lonesome wanderer on earth, Mr. Navarre dwindles into nothing more than just a chatty world-traveler. Certainly his expensive shoes never would have left in the dirt, had he ever walked there, any such definite message for me as did Jerry's naked feet. Those footprints, and the blue bag, were my signals that winter had packed up and gone away. I knew then that it was time to look for white bloodroot on the wooded slopes along the railroad tracks, the yellow flowers of adder's-tongues trembling between their narrow mottled leaves, and the tiny, scentless cups of hepaticas with stems so frail that I could scarcely bear to break them.

CHAPTER XVIII

THIRTEEN

ONE winter morning my mother was alone in the kitchen making me a cake for my thirteenth birthday. The two Negro women, big, hearty Sally and diminutive Virginia, who had long since supplanted Hannah, were at work upstairs in the front of the house. They were always pleased to be away from the kitchen, because the windows on one side gave a good view of the old burying-ground, and even by day the close presence of the ancient dead seemed to make them uneasy. This particular morning, however, they would have seen but little of those projecting stones, for they were half-buried in snow, and the trees stood rigid in the windless, glittering air.

The bright sun flooded in across the wide strip of polished copper above the sink and flashed in the stones of my mother's rings, which she had taken off before beginning her task and had laid in a little heap on the table before her. Over her gray woolen dress she wore one of the big lavender aprons that Sarah Stone always made for her, and as she stepped about the room she could see its clean color reflected in the mirror above the oak cabinet. Now and then she hummed softly to herself, for she liked to be alone in her own kitchen, and whatever she undertook there was with the fervor and vision, the careful attention to detail, of a superlative artist.

She scorned all but the finest materials, and the result must have a special shape, a particular taste, and a certain texture, or out it went and she began again. On this occasion she had already discarded one cake that did not suit these requirements, and for the second time was breaking eggs, the yokes into a white bowl, the whites into a yellow one, moving quietly and quickly and with an air of passionate devotion, almost like that of a priestess performing a sacred ritual. The table was crowded with plates bearing mounds of flour, sugar, and butter; there were cups of measured nuts, raisins, and sliced citron, and the air was sweet with the odors of spices and wines.

From the time when, as a slender child, she had wanted to make all by herself some contribution to send along in a box to her brother Philip in the army, she had loved to make a cake. But now the slender child, and the willowy young woman as well, had long ago disappeared. Instead she stood, stirring the batter in the bowl, a middle-aged woman, full-figured but still proudly erect, with gray hair white at the temples, and her hands, once so small and tapering, now knotted at the joints and out of shape. She would look at them ruefully sometimes and say, "It's not my fault. It's because my grandfather and my great-grandfather drank too much good port."

At this moment, as always, she wore at her throat a brooch that held in its beaded oval the miniature of that very great-grandfather, the Revolutionary surgeon. Her own face, with its blue eyes so quick to light with laughter or anger, the high-bred nose and the small mouth above the decisive chin, was faintly and femininely like the tiny painting in the pin. But most often her friends would tell her that she looked like Martha Washington. Then she would say scornfully, "That pudding-face!" But if a friend hastily changed to, "Well, Marie Antoinette, then," she would smile and say nothing. She would have liked to think that she resembled a queen.

After the second mixture had been baked and turned out on a plate, it proved to be perfect enough even for Mary Hale's daughter on her thirteenth birthday. She stood happily surveying it, her face flushed and her eyes sparkling. Hearing a step on the back porch, she glanced up at the clock, remembering that the boy from the butcher's was due with his packages. But when she turned to the door, she saw instead the figure of the old Jew, who came periodically and persistently nosing around almost as if he could smell the treasure trove of fading papers and worn clothes that lay stored away in the attic. He stood there before her, shivering in the icy air, huddled into his sagging overcoat that was green with age, his shabby derby hat jammed down over his impassive, patriarchal face.

"Any rags? Any rags? Any old clo'es? Any old papers? Any rags?" he chanted plaintively.

The plea seemed to come from some remote place far behind the surface of his eyes—hooded and watchful as an old bird's—and blown beseechingly through the tangle of his long beard. When she shook her head he bowed abjectly, but still hesitated hopefully as if he could read her thoughts, as if he followed them as they wandered through the house and up the two flights of stairs to those spaces under the eaves which were so crowded to overflowing with all that he desired. Any old clothes, any old papers? Why, she could have shown him a paradise had she so chosen. Instead she said, "No," quite firmly, and closing the door, turned away, her nostrils quivering from contact with his Old World aroma. She saw the shadow of his bowed shoulders under the grotesque hat pass her curtained windows as he plodded along the drive, and could not help but smile.

"Blessed are the meek," she murmured, and picking up her rings from the table, slipped them back upon her fingers.

That night my cake came to the table wreathed in smilax and white carnations, its pink candles brightly burning. My mother watched me with her slightly quizzical gaze as, making my wish, I blew out the candles and stood up to cut with great earnestness and pride the fruity, frosted slices.

"Now you are in your teens," she said. "Soon you will be a grown-up young woman."

That year in June, both Ned and I began to feel far beyond childhood when we went up to Hartford for commencement at Trinity College, where Sam was graduating. Ned had on his first pair of long trousers, and we were allowed to sit up very late and to drink our brother's health in small sips of champagne.

Trinity's gray stone buildings stood on the outskirts of the city, a small college, though an ancient one with traditions of its own. It had once been Washington College, where my grandfather had gone in his young manhood, but had changed its name. The commencement exercises were held outdoors, the senior class, which consisted of about twenty young men, seated in their "Morris chairs" in a semicircle on the grass. During the afternoon each one of them received a gift that was a good-natured joke on some trait in his character. To our astonishment, Sam's proved to be an imitation bomb, black and dangerous-looking, with a paper fuse fluttering from one end. His eyes twinkling, he stood up to take it in his hands, a little self-conscious in his cap and gown but obviously delighted to hear his friends saying with a chuckle to one another:

"Sam, the old Socialist!"

"What is it that Sam is?" I whispered to my father. He leaned toward me, smiling as he answered:

"I guess your brother must be 'agin the government.'"

I was still mystified, nor did it enlighten me to hear my mother's rather sharp comment:

"Yes, it's true that Sam has perfect confidence in all his own opinions."

I had heard her say that before, but it had been in connection with religion and the fact that Sam had successfully avoided all her attempts to guide him toward confirmation. Far more than her other children, she felt that he needed her church and her faith to support him through a life that was doomed to so cruel and so inescapable a desolation. Yet he was the one whose lips closed most stubbornly against repeating the creed. He would look at her with his straight gaze and say pitilessly:

"The resurrection of the body! That's a fine thing to ask *me* to believe in."

Probably my mother had only the most confused ideas, if any, about Socialism. But at least the bomb was a public acknowledgment that others as well as herself, though not with her consternation and fear, were aware of Sam's firm decision to go his own way no matter what he destroyed as he went.

That summer was Sam's last vacation before he went to work, and mine before I entered the Academy, the big high school down near the Park that was the next step in education after graduating from Miss Lucas's. Ned was already there, a year ahead of me, and both he and Sam delighted to tell me of the terrifying teachers, the hordes of pupils, and the profoundly difficult studies awaiting me in that ugly structure which reared its tall, mustard-colored walls beside the red Museum building. I had never been inside the Academy, but I knew the Museum. Miss Hattie Pinkham, a girlish spinster who taught drawing to some of Miss Lucas's pupils, had taken me there to introduce me to the statues of the gods and the heroes. She was somewhat surprised to find that they were old friends of mine, as I had never forgotten the winter afternoons with Hannah and her mythology book in the old kitchen.

Hannah had long since left our household, incredibly to marry and have her own home, thereby losing her sacred right to be, in the end, buried among the Hales. Her desertion was one of the innumerable little breaks in our tradition that might have shown us, had we stopped to notice them, how our whole world was changing. Even Norwich Town itself had begun to assume some unbecoming modern airs. River Road was now called Town Street; instead of going for our mail ourselves to the post office on the Green, it was delivered twice a day by a postman in a blue uniform; and soon electric street lights would make it no longer necessary for Ned to light each evening the old square kerosene lamp that stood at the entrance to our drive. (He, for one, did not deplore such signs of progress.) And if my grandfather had lived to be a hundred, as he had so longed to do, he would have seen far stranger machines in the streets of Norwich than bicycles. There were other, subtler differences too, which were to be more far-reaching than we could possibly have foreseen.

One afternoon in that July Sam and I sat on the front porch drinking ginger ale and chatting. The heat was breathless, and Ned, in a state of increasing discomfort and irritation, had gone off with Beany for a swim in Green's Pond. The maple trees stood unstirring, and the sky's blue, so clear in the morning, was now overlaid with leaden sullenness. Down in the meadow Mr. Burrill was cutting the hay, and there was something almost unbearable in that metallic sound striking through the stillness. As he shouted to his horses his voice seemed strained and uneasy, and the horses pulled through the field as heavily as if they were walking through water. Suddenly, I said:

"Sam, I think I hear thunder," and he laughed as he answered:

"Well, it always rains, doesn't it, as soon as Old Man Burrill starts his mowing."

Two carpenters walked up the road past the house, and turned in at Miss Bateman's gate. After a while they set up ladders and went up to the roof, which needed repairing. Their voices were more distinct than they knew on such a hot, quiet day, and presently we heard one say to the other in a low tone:

"Them folks next door here—name of Hale—ben there a long time, I understand. Ain't they Pilgrims, or Puritains, or sunthin'?"

His companion spat into the vines on the porch below. "Oh, sure," he said. "Ben there since the year one. But you know, Joe, that sorta stuff ain't so well thought on as 'twas onct. Them Pilgrims now . . ." His voice trailed off, overborne by a sudden spurt of clattering in the meadow as Mr. Burrill started down the long side of the field.

Sam and I looked at one another, grinning. It did not disturb us in the least to hear ourselves belittled by so surly a voice. There we sat in the shade of our grandfather's trees, under the shelter of the roof where all of us, from Felicity down, had been "since the year one," and where we felt sure that we would continue to be world without end. Hoyts and Hales, we would have said, were as inseparable a part of Norwich Town as the Meeting House Rocks, or the earth of the ancient burying-ground beyond our garden wall. We might have heard more of the carpenters' conversation, but just then my mother called to me from the upstairs window of my room:

"Come up and tell me what to do with all your old schoolbooks from Miss Lucas's. You won't be using them any more, and they clutter up your table so."

In my room she and I debated for a moment, pretending that there was really some choice in the matter. But we both knew well enough that the books would be put away in the attic. So, piling them in my arms, I went up there and set them on a shelf beside Sam's and Ned's. The same shelf held some of my mother's and Uncle Philip's and even a few of my grandfather's. As I arranged the books in a row, it never occurred to me that I was putting away something of myself in the attic too, and that the child who had been so carefree at Miss Lucas's—and also petted, and a little spoiled—was now as outgrown as her books. Instead, I turned and looked around at the rest of the attic, wishing I could stay there for a while. But it was a stifling place on a summer afternoon. The air in that space under the rafters would be as solid as stone, and beneath its weight you could almost feel the old papers and clothes and furniture crumbling into dust.

There were to come other times—not just in summer

but at any season—when the attic of itself and its own climate would press down upon my heart so heavily that I seemed to smother. But those times were still long years ahead of me. Now, as I stood there in the heat wiping my moist face against a gingham sleeve, I only knew that I longed to hear the cool rain beating on the roof and running along the eaves. That was the kind of a day for the attic, when outside the window streaming with silver the treetops rocked, softly moaning, and the wind went around the house in the same track that it had taken time out of mind. That was the weather when the attic could evoke a mood of elegy, a wistfulness for what was gone, a "heartbreak over fallen things." Even in hours of resentment, boredom, and rebellion, I could still be hushed into that mood again and again.

I never needed to wonder if I actually saw around me any awesome, glittering presences. Surely there is no ghost so substantial as the writing of a hand. There, on the paper spread out before you, you have all the resurrection that you can bear of the naked heart and the revealed mind. And sometimes even the tone of the voice rises up to you softly and beseechingly, or the hand that once held the pen touches your own with simple, eternal human tenderness.

Often I would not look into the letters at all, or so much as open a drawer. I would stand where the rough column of the chimney rose up through the center of the room, resting one hand on the harsh surface of the stones. Then it seemed as though something—perhaps the rain—started weaving, and I would find myself looking not at rafters and a slanting roof, but into a tapestry that hangs all around the shadowy room. It is silvery-green, and on it appears, like a repeated pattern, the outlines of the landscape that I knew, the hills and meadows, the small curving river and the iron bridge, the burying-ground amid its weeping-willow trees, the Green with its surrounding white houses, its rocky cliff and straight, steepled meeting-house.

These were all nothing more than my own dim imaginary murals. They were less material than cobwebs, but they were to abide with me for a long time. Even after the attic had been swept bare, its contents gone up in smoke from cleansing fire, and the house forsaken by its family, and the landscape stripped and disenchanted—even then they were to abide. Anywhere on earth I could restore for myself those archaic figures against their background of pale colors whenever there was rainfall over a roof and I happened to be under it, listening and alone.

In the foreground is our own doorway, where we stand, a family group like a picture from an album, my brothers and myself, my mother, and my father. Apart from us, ahead of us, one hand on a post at the front gate, my grandfather lifts his head under the branches of the maple trees, an old man looking quietly into the setting sun. His shadow, thrown back up the walk, reaches just to our feet, and darkens them.

The doorway and the gate reappear often in the whole design, but with different figures: a young soldier in a blue uniform waving a farewell, a woman shrouded under heavy black veils with a prayer book in her hands, and at her side a graceful child—a little girl—in crinoline. In one place on the tapestry the door stands open, and there in a room an elderly and stately lady sits in a pine writing-chair writing a letter. Behind her hangs the portrait of a fair-haired young man in a ruffled neckcloth.

This book has been printed in Estienne
type with Delphian initials.